"RICHIES"

A History of

THOMAS RICHARDSON & SONS

and

RICHARDSONS, WESTGARTH & CO. LTD.

1832—1994

Published by
Hartlepool Borough Council
1994

Dedication

This book is dedicated to my wife Elizabeth, without whose support and forbearance it would never have been completed; and to all those whose willing help has enabled the work to reach this stage.

© Peter L. Hogg, FICS

ISBN 0 9501306 6 4

Printed by
Ords Limited, Tower House, Tower Street, Hartlepool, Cleveland TS24 7HJ

Foreword

The marine engine builders of The Hartlepools were major employers of labour in the towns for many years, and trained a very large number of excellent engineers. It seemed sad to me that the story of this local works had not been written, which is how this book came to be born. My family background has strong maritime links, and my career was spent as a shipbroker in the port: my work brought me into contact with Richardsons, for whom my Company chartered many ships for the movement of heavy and indivisible loads from the works. I was (and am) acquainted with a number of people who were employed at both the local engine works and though not an engineer, I acquired some modest knowledge of what they made. It is my hope that this book will be a tribute to all who have been involved, at whatever level, in the manufacture of the high-quality machinery, both marine and land, for which our local engineers earned a well-deserved reputation.

Peter L. Hogg, FICS

Contents

The Castle Eden Origin

Thomas Richardson (I), born about 1795, was employed by the Earl of Durham in connection with the woodlands on his several estates in the Durham area. In 1832 Richardson took a 21 year lease (at £15 per annum) on land at Castle Eden to start an iron-working business — blacksmith work and the manufacture of cast iron objects, probably to serve the nearby collieries. At this time Hartlepool was promoting its Railway Bill, and the site chosen for Richardson's small works was at the junction of the Stockton to Durham turnpike road and the line of the railway from the nearby collieries to the reviving port of Hartlepool. Richardson was involved in the opening of a number of local collieries, and has been said to have been one of the pioneers of shipping coal from the newly revived port of Hartlepool.

The demand for machinery of all kinds was growing apace at that time, and the works seems to have expanded fairly rapidly. Before long it was necessary to instal a beam-type steam engine to supply power to the machinery in the shops — by shafting with belt-drive to the individual machines.

The Castle Eden enterprise prospered and advanced to the building of rail locomotives, as well as winding engines and other plant for collieries.

Some rail locomotive engines have been attributed to Richardsons at Hartlepool from early dates, as is the 1845 'Conside' locomotive for the Stockton & Darlington Railway. We shall probably never know if these were made by the original Hartlepool Iron Works (founded about 1838) or by Richardsons at Castle Eden. If the dates are right, then they were certainly not built at the Richardson works in Middleton, as those premises were only acquired by them in 1847.

The "Ballast Engine", used for many years in West Hartlepool Docks to haul wagons of ship ballast for dumping on the marshy ground to the south of the docks, was built by Thomas Richardson at Castle Eden, according to Robert Martin in his "History of West Hartlepool and its Founder", which carries a drawing of the engine.

After Thomas Richardson (I) took up a lease of the Hartlepool Iron Works in Middleton in 1847, and moved to the new site much of his work, the Castle Eden works continued (described as being in "co-partnership" with the newly acquired premises at Middleton) until shortly before the 21-year lease at Castle Eden was due to expire. In April 1853 what remained of the plant & machinery was sold off and the lease expired a few months later. By this time, of course, Richardsons were operating a flourishing iron-working business at Middleton.

THE OLD BALLAST ENGINE

The Hartlepool Iron Works

Before the revival of the port of Hartlepool took place, Middleton, on the opposite shore of the tidal harbour from Hartlepool, was a hamlet with 2 windmills, a few houses, including Middleton House, and little else. Joseph Parkin & Thomas Richardson, having built their first (wooden) ships inside Hartlepool Town Wall, moved their shipbuilding activity to the Middleton shore in 1838, and this, with Hartlepool Iron Works, was the start of any industrial activity (apart from milling) on the site, though there was at one stage (probably post-1850) a Bottle Works there, owned by Walkers of Middleton House. The land for the shipyard had been bought from Walkers, in 1838, and so presumably had the site of the Hartlepool Iron Works.

Hartlepool Iron Works had been started about 1838 on the Middleton shore by colliery owners and local investors, including Stephen Robinson, Thomas Belk and George Green, with the aim of providing much of the mechanical equipment needed by the port of Hartlepool as its local coal shipments began to grow substantially. Robinson was an engineer and his designs for apparatus to discharge solid ballast from ships and for loading coal from the little 'chaldron' wagons then in use are to be found in Cuthbert Sharp's "History of Hartlepool". In 1842 Robinson issued a specification for railway engines which brought coal to the port of Hartlepool, and he was the designer of the 1847 lighthouse on the Heugh. Stephen Robinson was Mayor of Hartlepool in 1851: Thomas Belk, a solicitor, was then Hartlepool's Town Clerk.

There is little solid evidence remaining of the output from the works in their original ownership, but almost certainly some rail locomotives were built there for the Hartlepool Dock & Railway Co., and possibly for collieries which shipped via the port. Lowe and others quote Nos. 104 and 105 of 1840, but the reliability of that information is uncertain.

The proprietors of the Iron Works agreed in 1847 to lease the works to Thomas Richardson, and it was so leased until the year 1864, when Richardson bought the works. The business had expanded considerably by that time, and from then on he made several acquisitions of land at Middleton to extend the works, including, in 1882, Christopher Walker's Bottle Works. Additional land was taken on lease in 1847 from the Railway Company, and further areas near the works were leased later. The configuration of Middleton in 1858 is shown in the Slater-Calver survey of that year.

In 1847 the beam engine which had been in use at Castle Eden to supply power by belt drive to the machine shops had been moved to Middleton, and an 1894 report states that it was then still in use, and the man who installed it at Middleton (appropriately named Mr. B. Wright) was in 1894 the Chief Foreman of the Engineering Sections of Richardsons. By then it must have been some 50 years old, and Mr. Wright considerably older.

Richardson's Early Production at Middleton

This consisted at first of winding engines, blast engines and locomotives, as well as many other lines of cast and wrought iron work. At least one item of their 1851 production is still clearly visible and identifiable today at the Moorhouse Estate, near Preston Park: a cast-iron bridge beam. Several authorities have stated that the works numbers started at 101 and that the first three were stationary engines, the first locomotive being No. 104. Numbers for marine engines produced before 1899 have not so far been traced.

In 1851 Richardsons produced what was probably their first commercial marine engine — this was a 30 IHP engine for a paddle tug built in Sunderland and owned at the time by Richardsons and their bankers (Backhouse). In 1852 the tug was sold to Benjamin Henderson Huntley, a Chester-le-Street man who had moved to Hartlepool and went on to own a number of tugs as well as other vessels.

Thomas Richardson (I), the founder of the enterprise, who died in 1850, had built the small wooden sloop "Isabel" (50 feet long and 45 tons register) in 1837 on the banks of the Slake, and B. G. Spaldin believes that this vessel could have been used as a testbed for marine engines. Thomas Richardson (III), in a speech made in the 1890's, referred to her as a steam vessel, although she had definitely been built as a sailing ship.

TR (I) was succeeded in 1850 by TR (II), his eldest son, who had been brought up in the business from an early age.

This was a time when the marine steam engine was beginning to move out of the low speed paddle engine to the higher speed (50-80 rpm) required for screw propulsion, where the future of steam at sea lay. Wooden vessels, which flexed in a seaway, were not suited to screw propulsion with its long propeller-shaft: the rigidity of a metal hull was needed for screw steamers.

There was an enormous expansion in the number of steam vessels on the British register from 1840 to 1874: clearly there was room for shipbuilders and engine-builders to support the demand for steamers.

The Richardson Brothers (Thomas (II) and John William) built the first iron ship in Hartlepool in 1855 (this was the "Sir Colin Campbell" — a screw collier) and several of the early Thomas Richardson engines went into tonnage built in the Middleton shipyard, founded 1838 by transfer of operations across the channel from Old Hartlepool. The press reported that the "Sir Colin Campbell", which was named after a military hero of the Crimean War, was launched complete with engines and boiler.

However, by 1857 the shipbuilding operations were in serious financial difficulty, with liabilities some £30,000 over their assets, and operations ceased. The ironworks was a separate operation and was unaffected by that failure.

Marine Engineering Practice to about 1857

Up to about 1842 no large marine engines had been built for more than about 20 rpm. Brunel had to use chain wheels as a "multiplying gear" to get 56 rpm for the "Great Britain". By 1842 the problem was being overcome for such ships as the "Bedlington" collier of 277 Gross Tons, built by T. D. Marshall of South Shields.

A Parliamentary Commission of 1839 had declared very firmly that there was no advantage in the use of "high pressure steam" — by that I think we can assume they meant above about 10 to 15 pounds. But the engineers knew better, now that they had learned to use steam expansively, thanks to James Watt.

The growth of the steam collier trade to the Thames alone gives an indication of how things progressed: — In 1852 screw colliers had made only 17 voyages to London with coals, delivering 9843 tons, but by 1862 the year's figures were 1472 voyages — 950,000 tons. This, clearly, was a band-wagon to be on.

The coastal coal trade was not the only one to be increasing rapidly — all seaborne trade in the world was expanding sharply.

The reader may find it helpful to have some explanation of Nominal Horsepower and Indicated Horse Power. The former is calculated from the engine dimensions and steam pressure — rather like the old RAC formula for car engines which was the basis of the licensing system not so very long ago. Indicated is from the indicator diagram and is nearer to the modern Brake Horse Power: the IHP was the same as NHP for the earlier engines, rising to about 3 x NHP for the simple engine, and the disparity gradually got greater with more efficient engines until the later triples had an IHP about 6 times their NHP. Engineers argued about the definition of power output for many years.

Although the simple engine, with its single expansion, was very much the standard production, the two cylinder compound marine engine, using a further expansive stage, was in the wings. Randolph & Elder of Glasgow are credited with the first marine version, in the "Brandon" in 1854, though they had already made stationary engines on that principle. Even with steam at only 30 pounds (due to boiler materials and technology) it showed a fuel saving of 30-40% over the simple engine. "Brandon" consumed about 3.25lbs of fuel per IHP per hour — as against 4.0 to 4.5lbs for the simple engine.

In 1855 Marshall had quoted as best practice the screw steamer "Brigadier", with a simple engine of 210 NHP at a steam pressure of 15 pounds, the shaft speed being 70 rpm.

The jet condenser, which was very inefficient and wasteful, was replaced from about 1859 with the surface condenser, which was a great improvement. It was more or less 're-invented' by Hawthorns, as Hall's surface condenser of 1839 had apparently been forgotten, as had Marc Brunel's of 1843.

The condenser's task was to produce as high a vacuum as possible at the back end of the steam engine, thus adding a theoretical maximum of 14 pounds to the very low steam pressures of the day. The surface condenser had the merit that it conserved the condensate for feed water to the boiler. The use of salt water as feed for the boilers at sea gradually built up the salt content of the boiler water, causing glazing of the heating surfaces, (which adversely effected heat transfer) and frothing on the surface which led to "Priming" — water getting to the cylinders, with consequent problems. While the surface condenser gave better vacuum and conserved some condensate for feed, make-up water was still needed, and until more output was available from boilers the evaporator could not be introduced into the system, to supply fresh water and so eliminate the need for using sea-water as make-up feed, to the benefit of the boilers. The evaporator produced fresh water from seawater, but consumed steam in doing so.

In the period 1851 to 1861 the average marine engine was of 310 IHP, working at 40 pounds. Even as late as 1858 John Elder of Glasgow, refers in a patent application of 1858 (No. 162) to the increased advantage of using "what is generally considered high pressure steam, that is to say of a pressure of twenty pounds or upwards per square inch".

Later Single Expansion Engines
(Simple Engines)

George W. Jaffrey was brought to Hartlepool in 1855 from the works of Tod & McGregor of Glasgow — a successful firm of engine builders. Jaffrey's 'patent triple-cylindrical engine' was fitted in 1856 to the vessels "Ireland" and 1857 "Armenian", from Richardson Brothers yard. This was Patent No. 652 of 1856. The engine had three cranks at 120 degrees, leading to economy, reduced stress and less vibration. It was still only a single expansion engine — each cylinder fed in turn from the boiler, and exhausting steam to the condenser. The Patent claimed at least one-third saving in fuel as well as reduced stresses and vibration. Why apparently no others made when the Masters of these vessels wrote such glowing testimonials? The "Ireland" was re-engined in 1867 by Palmers of Jarrow, but a new engine after 11 years was not uncommon in those days.

The Mercury of 26.12.1857 contained an extract from a letter sent from Calcutta on 6th November to Mr. George Jaffrey by Captain Fowler of the "Armenian", which is worth quoting: —

It is with pleasure I write that I am able to congratulate you on the success of your engines; they are admired by everyone here that sees them; and what is better still, WE KNOW they can work well, for they did us good service from Galle to Calcutta, being under steam for eight days in heavy weather, and never had to stop the whole time. As for the boiler, there is not a white mark from a leak on one of the rivets, and you can see the bare iron on the inside of the boiler, and also of the tubes. The steam was from 18 to 20lbs all the time, vacuum 13½lbs. She steams 6½ knots good in a calm, smooth sea, and this, I know, is not bad for 60 horsepower in a 1,000 ton ship. We sail from here on the 12th of next month for China with a cargo of opium, very valuable, and our owners expect us to do great things. All I can say is, if we do not succeed, it will not be the fault of your engines."

The "Chow Phya" of 1858 (John Pile's 6th steamer) was engined by TR — simple 2 cylinder of 34" with a 22" stroke. Steam at 16 pounds gave an average pressure across the engine of 24 psi Hartlepool/Southampton and 22 psi Southampton/Singapore. Jaffrey claimed it as very economical, quoting it as 836 IHP and using on the first leg 1.94 pounds per IHP per hour, and on the far longer second leg 2.18 pounds per IHP per hour. Then the boiler was steaming at 12lbs, and it was claimed that the condenser could reach 14lbs of vacuum, but the average was only 22 pounds across the engine. Engine revs are quoted as 75 rpm. It must be said that these coal consumption figures are remarkably better than anyone else was achieving at that time, so must be open to some doubt.

By 1861 it seems that the building of marine steam engines and their accessories was the main business of the company: engines and boilers were installed at a set of wooden sheerlegs on the Northgate side of the Victoria Dock.

In 1862 the Admiralty, having completed a close examination of the works, added Richardsons to their list of approved suppliers. The Hartlepool Free Press reported in August 1862 that Richardsons had built 19 sets of engines since July 1861.

Also in 1862 Richardsons engined the "Tynemouth", Sunderland-built, with engines and boiler — the latter fitted with a "new feed water heating apparatus on the multi-tubular principle designed by Mr. Jaffrey."

Denton Gray's first steamer, "Dessouk", was built in 1865 and engined by Richardsons, and later that year Denton Gray built the steamship "Malacca", which ship was at first owned in equal shares by Denton Gray & Thomas Richardson, who supplied her machinery.

In 1866, for shipowner George Pyman's "Lizzie English (1)", with a simple engine of 2 cylinders, each 38" diameter, the builders were guaranteeing "not less than 27 sq. feet of heating surface per NHP".

In 1868 two new vessels had a race Whitby — Tees and back, and a lengthy report in the local "Mercury" gives Richardsons the credit for the better performance of the "Ebor", which was engined by him. The other was not.

The election propoganda of 1868, when Thomas Richardson (II) was opposing Ward Jackson, claimed Richardson was "by far the largest employer in the Hartlepools". This is not surprising, for by this time he had acquired the West Hartlepool Rolling Mills & Blast Furnaces of Pile Spence, who went down in the banking crisis of 1866. He was unsuccessful in that election (by 3 votes), but in 1874 entered Parliament for The Hartlepools. He soon had to resign, for reasons which are explained later, but was elected again in 1880 and again in 1886.

Thomas Richardson (III), son of Thomas Richardson (II), joined the business in 1868 after school and Cambridge University.

Denton Gray built the "Moldavia" for Richardsons' own account in 1869 and Richardson engined her — he paid for the ship with two engine sets for Denton Gray to use in other vessels they were to build. The following year he did the same with the steamer "Thomas Hampton". From this we can deduce that the cost of the engines was about one third of the total cost — or equal to about one half of the cost of the ship's hull.

S.S. "GRANADIAN"   Pile Spence 1864

Photographs courtesy of the National Maritime Museum, Greenwich.

S.S. "DESSOUK"   Denton Gray 1865

Page 8

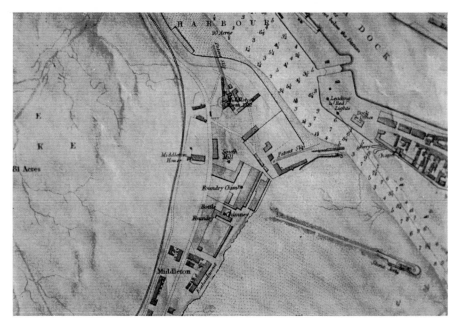

SLATER-CALVER SURVEY, 1858.

ENGINES OF THE STEAMSHIP EVORA.

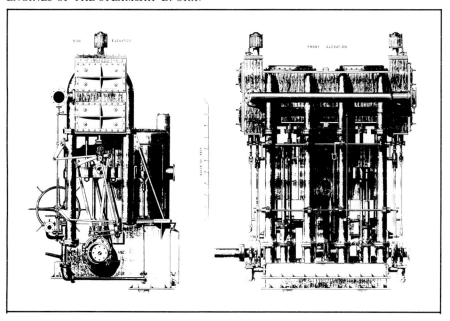

Page 9

These ships did not remain under Richardsons' ownership — they were sold on before very long. Denton Gray's "Euxine" was originally jointly owned by the builders and Thomas Richardson — she was later sold, re-named the "Great Northern" after conversion to an early cable-laying ship.

The two cylinder simple marine engine had, by 1870, reached the peak of its development, and a Richardson engine of 1870 was given an illustrated write-up in "The Engineer" of that year. The ship concerned was the Sunderland built "Evora" (displacement 3000 tons) and the article gave details of the engine and its performance at sea. It was a simple engine of 250 NHP, with two cylinders each 48" diameter and of 42" stroke. The construction system of the engine was "designed by Mr. Jaffrey", and the ship had two 'circular' (presumably cylindrical) boilers each 11'6" diam. and 10'6" long, with vertical water tubes in the firebox. Each had three furnaces, giving 3234 sq. ft. of heating surface, and the steam pressure was 50 pounds. Surface condensers were fitted, and there was some kind of early superheater, heating the steam to a higher temperature as it left the boilers. Consumption was 13.25 tons per 24 hours steaming. She was on the London-Calcutta service, via Malta, Port Said, Suez, Colombo and Madras. The round voyage, port to port, took almost 92 days, which appears to be an average of 7.5 knots: rather high for the times, perhaps.

N.E.R. MAP 1864.

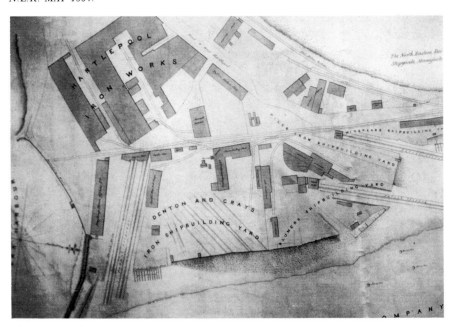

The Two Cylinder Compound Engine

It was from 1870 that the compound engine was widely adopted for marine use, after the Liverpool shipowner Alfred Holt had designed his own and showed how it led to economy of fuel. His "Cleator" of 318 GRT (1864) was used as a test-bed and with boilers at 60 pounds, was faster on 40% less fuel with her new Holt engine. There was parallel development by Glasgow engineers at the same time.

As a direct result of the "Cleator" performance Holt built three ships each carrying some 3500 tons ('Agamemnon', 'Ajax' and 'Achilles') in 1864-5 for his Far East service, fitted with his design of tandem compound engines, showing excellent economy on their service route UK/China via Cape of Good Hope. Incidentally, when the Suez Canal opened in 1869 he was ideally placed to profit by that shortening of his established route.

As at this time the cost of coal represented some 18% of the running costs of a ship (figures based on a ship carrying 2500 tons) significant economies in consumption were clearly a desirable goal at which to aim.

Even now there was little or no possibility of running at higher steam pressures owing to the continued use of wrought iron for the boilers. This material was very much less strong, weight for weight, than mild steel — and could only be made in modest sized plates. The factor which allowed high pressures was the use of mild steel for their construction, from the late 1870's. The first steel marine boiler from Tyneside was built at Wallsend: the material was Siemens steel from the Landore Works in South Wales. Mild steel then cost about £14 per ton, and its price fell only slowly to reach about £6 per ton by 1893.

Richardsons' first two-cylinder compound engine was probably that installed in the "Kepier", Sunderland built, in 1869, presumably after a period of testing the new type of engine. It was not until 1874 that Lloyd's Register began to show details of ship's engines, so being sure of the early vessels is not easy, and if they were lost or changed their name before 1874 it is even more difficult.

Richardsons' last two-cylinder simple marine engine was probably that made in 1875 for the Tyne-built "Killingworth".

Much of Richardsons' 1870 production was of two-cylinder compound engines; listings show 30 sets produced in 1870 for ships from no less than eight different yards — 12 simple and 18 compound. By the year 1872 they had advanced them to the stage at which they would give guarantees such as that given to the owners of the locally built "Tertia" (for German owners) that the 100 NHP Compound engine would give 450 IHP at 65 pounds from her double-ended boiler. A surface condenser was fitted. The cylinders were of 27 and 50 inches diameter with a stroke of 33 inches. One may assume that shipowners were demanding that kind of assurance from the engine suppliers, and this probably tells us something about unsatisfactory engines from some engine-builders.

The press of 1871 reports 1300 men employed at Richardsons, and one ship engined that year was the "Acacia" from the Denton Gray yard, with a compound of 100 NHP which cost £45 per NHP—i.e. £4,500 complete with boilers and auxiliaries.

For the "Atalante" of 1872, also from the Denton Gray yard, they guaranteed 8.5 knots in smooth water, fully laden, on 9.6 tons of coal per day. This was a Compound engine of 115 NHP. Richardsons said that if 8 knots was not sustainable in smooth water the contract would be void, and penalties were specified for performance falling between the two extremes. That ship would have carried about 1600 tons of cargo—she was 235 feet long.

In 1872 the Board of Trade expressed serious doubts as to the wisdom of using steam at pressures over 70 psi in merchant ships. The number of boiler explosions would no doubt have influenced their view, and it was some time before steam pressures at sea were generally much in excess of that figure.

This was a year in which Richardsons sold 20 sets of engines and boilers and in which Thomas Mudd, a brilliant engineer, joined the firm from Darlington Forge: he was then only 20 years old.

Shipowners' desire for fuel economy created a good deal of work for Richardsons converting simple engines to compound, and they developed (as did other engine builders) effective ways of using part of the existing plant to make a 2-cylinder Compound engine. In effect they replaced one cylinder with a new HP cylinder and its associated valve gear. A new boiler and auxiliaries were usually included in the order. Both Robert Wyllie and Donald Morison of Richardsons had devised methods for up-rating or converting older engines.

In 1873 the Tees built "Kong Sverre" came round to Hartlepool for Richardson engines and boilers; in this case a 310 NHP compound engine with cylinders 39 and 75 inches diameter (39" stroke) which were installed at the wooden sheerlegs at Victoria Dock—in use then for many years. The wooden sheers broke while lifting a 27 ton boiler into the ship and were replaced on the same site with iron sheers.

In 1879 J. Sterling Begbie, an engineering consultant, writing to Glasgow shipbuilders Denny on engine performance and availability, said of the Hartlepool engine makers:

"Richardsons' stroke is shorter than most, and his boiler is smaller, but no-one beats him for consumption and speed: there is an advantage to the owner in point of the smaller weight of water carried. He has 9 contracts in hand, 6 of them not touched, and cannot offer delivery under 12 months. He got about 4% reduction in wages all round recently."

Glasgow engineers were pointing the way ahead for marine engines: in 1882 Napiers engined a newly built vessel ("Aberdeen") for the Australia run, using double-ended cylindrical steel boilers steaming at the then relatively high pressure of 125 pounds. That ship had an early Glasgow triple expansion engine and, it was claimed, achieved the low consumption of 1.25lbs of coal per IHP per hour.

In 1882 Richardsons gained room for further expansion by the acquisition of Christopher Walker's Bottle Works at Middleton. In that same year James Bower left Richardsons to take up the post of Engine Designer with Martens, Olsen & Co. of Norway, later moving to become a Director of Laxevaags at Bergen, a shipyard which developed its own engine works.

We have to remember that until reliable engines of reasonable horsepower were available at an acceptable cost, and of weight which did not reduce too much the ship's earning ability, the engine was to some extent an auxiliary and sails were used much of the time for the propulsive effort, though this was even more true of the days of the simple engine, before 1870.

The shipowner had to bear in mind several factors, including the fuel consumption—which in turn reflected upon the weight of fuel carried and the strokehold staff needed—the weight of the boilers and engines, and the space in the ship which they and the bunker coals occupied, as cargo intake with low density cargoes depended on internal hold space rather than on deadweight cargo carrying capacity.

Clearly there was a substantial commercial prize for producing engines which were more economical and lighter than those of the competition—and if they could occupy less room in the ship, even better.

CRANK SHAFT, S.S. ROSLIN CASTLE.

The Triple Expansion Engine

This had arrived on the marine scene in 1880, in s.s. "Propontis", as an experiment with an engine designed by Dr. Kirk. Unfortunately, the boilers could not supply the higher pressure steam needed for the proper use of three expansions, but the start had been made. "Propontis" was by no means the first ship to be let down by her boilers. The first Tyne built triple came from Wallsend Slipway in 1882 to a design by Alex Taylor.

Richardsons produced their first in 1883, but were still supplying marine compound engines for several years after that date. Thus, while not in the van of progress, they were not far behind.

This type of engine, using the steam in three successive expansions, proved very efficient — certainly compared with the compound engines which had been the norm for the last 13 years or so. Without the higher boiler pressures then obtainable (160 to 180 pounds due to better materials and design features) there would have been little point in trying to obtain a third stage of expansion, even although condensers had improved to the point where they could produce consistently over 28 inches of mercury vacuum — about 12 pounds. Improvements were being made in packing materials used for the piston rods and rings and this reduced losses in that direction.

As time went on, sustainable piston speeds became higher, due to better lubricants of mineral oils, improved piston rings and finer machined finishes on the cylinder walls, from the advances in machine tools.

TR's first triple (1883) had cylinders 19, 35 and 53 inch diameter with a 33 inch stroke. The rating of this engine was 150 NHP (700 IHP), installed in the well-decker "Para" for Steel Young & Co. of London. Note that the ratio of NHP to IHP is now 4.6. The horsepower figures may not be totally reliable, but show the way triples were shaping.

In 1881 partial electric lighting was introduced into the works and the following year Thomas Mudd left at the instigation of William Gray, who had decided, very bravely, to start his own engine works. Richardsons, of course, were faced with the threat of local competition in addition to that already existing from the numerous engine builders on the Wear, Tyne and Tees — Blairs of Stockton had engined many Hartlepool built ships.

When Rendell surveyed the port for improvements in 1884 his plans show Middleton in some detail and have given us a record of how the works had grown by that date.

The marine output for 1886 was 12 sets, totalling 30,050 IHP plus a large triple expansion engine and pumps for the East London Water Co., which achieved much publicity in the technical press. Pumps of various kinds had long been produced by TR — first no doubt for collieries, then the necessary air circulating and feed pumps for engines and, as early as 1853, a steam-driven set to empty John Pile's drydock in six hours.

From 1885 Richardsons were "tripling" a series of ships for Donald Currie's Union Line — "Anglian" was the first. This work involved the ingenious use of much of the existing two cylinder compound engine, and it was a very successful operation — Currie sent a series of his vessels to Hartlepool for conversion, and others did too. The "Grantully Castle", tripled in 1887, was reported by the Owners to have been a very successful conversion, showing a saving of some 24% (1.9lbs/IHP/Hr. reduced to 1.46lbs/IHP/Hr.). At the same time, of course, new sets of triples were being supplied and the 1887 output was 16 sets totalling 37,000 IHP.

In 1886 the works was partly rebuilt and by 1888, 1100 men were employed. The output for that year was reported as 12 ship sets, totalling 40,050 IHP, "and several sets for sending out". The latter phrase shows the difficulties in compiling a definite list of the marine engines produced by the firm. Further improvements in the works in 1888 comprised a new boiler shop, complete with an 80-ton travelling steam crane. In 1889 the output was 30 ship sets of 44,800 IHP.

Richardsons continued with their conversions of two-cylinder engines to triples and with re-engining as well as supplying triples for newbuildings. Their work for the Union Line of Donald Currie was given considerable publicity and when the "Roslin Castle" lay at the Sheerlegs on C Jetty she was open for inspection by the public for a while. She had already been lengthened by 15 feet with a new and "finer" stern shape by Withy's yard, Hartlepool. The technical press of the day featured some of these conversions in detail, so considerable data has survived.

This vessel's original compound engine was one of 50" and 90" x 60" stroke and the new one had same stroke with cylinders of 36", 60" and 96". Three new boilers steamed at 160 pounds — they were 17'9" long x 14'4" diameter. With the original Compound the consumption had been 1.9lbs per IHP per hour for a speed of 12.5 knots. Designed for better speed with new engine, she achieved an average of 14.5 knots Dartmouth — Madeira. Part of the original crankshaft was retained and a new section for the intermediate pressure cylinder was added — the whole was then bolted up and lathe-turned: it weighed 30 tons and was of 18" diameter.

In 1889 a new pattern shop was built, and in 1890 TR (II) died: by this time TR (III) — later to be Sir Thomas — was a man of 54 and well established in the business, with a considerable reputation.

HARTLEPOOL WORKS — BOILER SHOP.

HARTLEPOOL WORKS — PATTERN SHOP.

In that year the output was 33 ship sets, totalling 45,000 IHP. In addition, 132 cranks and propeller shafts were made and the forge output was 2250 tons of forgings, including 700 built crankshafts. It was stated that in the last 15 months the firm had sold 200 Morison Patent Evaporators. This last was made under one of the many patents taken out by D. B. Morison during his time at Richardsons.

By about 1891, the reciprocating steam engine had pretty well reached its peak performance and was a reliable source of power, but even so, some owners were still building quite large steamers with a considerable sail area, including some square sails in a few cases, usually as brig rig.

The quadruple expansion engine, which really needed steam at above 200 pounds, may have seemed a natural progression from triple (when boilers could sustain suitable high pressures) but it was a field Richardsons did not enter until many years later — well after the period covered by this paper — though Gray's Central Marine Engine Works was busy with them in the late 1880's, to designs by Thomas Mudd. Other engine makers were also producing quadruple expansion machinery. Some of Mudd's had two of the lowest pressure cylinders — five crank quadruple expansion engines.

Development work at Richardsons in the 1880-1890 period was (judging by local patents taken out at that time) largely concentrated on boilers and peripherals, presumably perceived as weak links in the chain.

Forced Draught came in and superheating (steam being further heated after generation in the boilers). The proponents of Forced Draught claimed a 15% saving in fuel, but perhaps more importantly, it allowed the better combustion of poor quality coals. By no means were all bunker coals, even some of those taken in the UK, anywhere nearly equal to "best Welsh steam coal", which was the yardstick for judging bunker coals. Even the better coals would have suffered degradation in the course of being shipped to distant bunkering stations and thus being handled several times before they reached the fireman's shovel.

For more efficient working new Sheerlegs were installed on the Middleton side of the North Basin in 1890, with direct access from the works.

In 1890, the "Engineer" published pictures of Richardsons' engine for the Hamburg & Calcutta Steamship Company's "Baria". This was a ship of about 4500 tons carrying capacity with a 304 NHP triple, with cylinders 24½, 38 and 64 inches and stroke of 48 inches. The boiler pressure was 160 pounds from two double-ended boilers with eight corrugated furnaces. The 'Morison' corrugated furnace was another Richardsons' patent.

In 1892, the "Stranton" and the "Pallion" were converted to triple expansion: these ships had been built more than 10 years before and engined with Richardson compounds, having 33" and 61" cylinders with a stroke of 33 inches: steam pressure was 75 pounds. The method of conversion, designed by D. B. Morison of Richardsons, made at least one text-book on Marine Engineering. A new High Pressure section was added, the Low Pressure cylinder given a liner to reduce its bore to 56" and the crankshaft extended for the new HP. Thus the two original cylinders were retained. New boilers steaming at 170 pounds, plus new feed, air and circulating pumps, new evaporator and condenser, completed the work.

By 1893, water tube boilers were being introduced by other boiler-makers, but these were principally for turbines, which Richardsons did not produce at this stage of their existence.

In the years 1897 to 1898, new electrical plant was installed in the Middleton works for the generation of Alternating Current on the 3-phase system. This was for the driving of machinery in the works. The alternators were from the Swiss firm of Brown-Boveri and the link with this outstanding Swiss firm was to be a long standing one. Richardsons were now able to offer steam-driven alternators for factory power units and immediately began to build up a considerable trade in this non-marine field, having been appointed sole representatives of the Swiss patentees Brown, Boveri. "The Steamship" of February 1899 reported that Richardsons had then a large number of orders in hand for such installations.

The initial generating plant cost some £15,000, but it enabled Richardsons to dispense with twenty separate engines and ten sets of boilers in the works, which had driven shafting to supply power to the machines in the various shops. Presumably, they would then have dispensed with the 1840's beam engine they had brought down from Castle Eden in 1847, if it had not already been scrapped. The savings in fuel and wages were expected to make the investment show a very short pay-back time.

The new generators were driven by a Corliss horizontal compound engine: two were installed, each with its own boiler at 160 pounds, and the two were used week and week about. There was also a smaller engine driving an 80 kilowatt alternator for night shift use. Thirteen motors of 10 HP to 65 HP were driven by the supply to operate machinery in the works and the total output was said to be about 1250 horse-power.

A turn of the century picture of Hartlepool Works shows two of their best-selling lines, expansion and condensers, ready for despatch. The sale of these items was a significant part of the works' output.

Not many records from Middleton have survived, but from other sources it has been possible to gain indications of the cost of marine engine sets, and these are given below.

Average costs have quoted as: —

1864 Simple engines with surface Condenser £38.25 per NHP

1867   £36.00

1868   £41.00   (with jet condenser £36)

1870 Simple engines with surface condenser £40.18

       Compound   "   "   "   "   £45.00   Boiler pressure 60-65 psi.

1882 Compound with surface condenser   £42.50

1888 Triple   "   "   "   £35.46

HARTLEPOOL WORKS — AUXILIARY DEPARTMENT.

BASIN QUAY AND SHEER LEGS.

Personalities

Thomas Richardson (I): 1795-1850: about 1820 he married Isabella Heslop. He died when the new enterprise at Middleton was only just started. His obituary in the Durham Chronicle says that *"as a master he was considerate and generous— thoughtful as to the wants of those in his employment, anxious to assist them in their necessities, and prompt in alleviating their sufferings. To promote the health of his numerous workmen, and to protect them from the demoralising influences of dissipation, he encouraged amongst them manly recreations and other amusements, which afford an agreeable and beneficial relaxation from their toils of labour, and which he frequently animated by his presence; while by establishing reading societies for their intellectual improvement, he showed himself no less desirous to facilitate their advancement in the higher fields of literature and science."* (One contemporary report hinted that Richardson had a financial stake in this journal).

Thomas Richardson (II) 1821-1890: in 1843 he married Maria Greenwell, the daughter of a Sunderland shipowner. He was apprenticed to his father and took control after his father's death in 1850, enlarging the size and activities of the works, both in iron-founding and engineering. He also dealt in ships, tending to buy and sell rather than manage them for any length of time. In 1867, for instance, he bought the "Cristobal Colon" from the liquidator when the owners went broke while she was being lengthened, re-engined her and soon sold her to the French Government as "Savoie". He was a Liberal politician and the local Member in 1874 briefly, again in 1880 and from 1886 until his death. From 1863 he was living in the Friarage, Yarm, rented from Thomas Meynell of the N.E.R. Later he occupied The Grange at Kirklevington and then built Kirklevington Hall, into which he moved in 1884. The last Richardson to occupy the Hall was the Rev. Charles Edward, son of Thomas (II), who was born in 1853 and died in 1940.

Thomas Richardson (III) 1846-1906: Born at Castle Eden. Married (in 1878) Anna Constance Cooke-Faber. He entered the business about 1868 after an education at Rossall School and a degree at Cambridge. Was made a Freeman of West Hartlepool in 1897 after Council service, and was knighted in 1898. He had seven sons and two daughters: it was a family tragedy that only two of the sons survived World War One and neither came into the business. The elder (Thomas) was a lawyer, later Judge Richardson ("The friendly judge"). The younger son to survive (Roland) was an accountant and in later life returned to manage the Boanson business in West Hartlepool founded by his late father-in-law. Sir Thomas lived at Kirklevington Grange.

George W. Jaffrey: 1820-1905: Born in London in 1820, he came to Hartlepool in 1855 from Glasgow (Tod & McGregor). An inventive engineer. In his early youth he was apprenticed to the shipbuilder Wingate of Glasgow. At age 11 he saw and took much interest in "Fairy Queen" — an early steamship on the Clyde. In 1838 he worked on engining "Sirlus" (Atlantic rival to Brunel's "Great Western"). Was Mayor of Hartlepool in 1867 and in 1868 — second time on his own casting vote. Returned to Tod & McGregor, Glasgow, in 1870 and died at Greenock in July 1905. Long after his return to Glasgow he published a memoir of his Hartlepool days: this reveals the various pen-names under which he wrote to local papers.

THOMAS RICHARDSON II   THOMAS RICHARDSON III   D. B. MORISON

Thomas Mudd: Born Kirby Fleetham 1852. Joined Richardsons in 1872 after starting at Darlington Forge. Left in 1882 to Central Marine Engine Works, a William Gray enterprise, and was responsible (age 30) for layout of new works: he was only 46 when he died at his home "Greencliffe", Cliff Terrace, Hartlepool, in May 1898 in office as Mayor of Hartlepool. An inventive engineer, whose early death was a sad blow to Central Marine and the town of Hartlepool.

Charles Smith: General Manager of TR for some years until his accidental death in 1882 while bathing in Lake Lucerne. He was succeeded by Robert Wyllie.

Robert Wyllie: A Scottish engineer who came from the noted firm of Elders, Glasgow. General Manager of TR from 1882 in succession to Charles Smith. Died in July 1886 after being injured in the fall of the Victoria Dock sheerlegs on 18th June 1886. His patented valve gear for triples was still in use when the Union vessels ("Castle" ships) were being tripled in 1887 onwards. (One of his daughters married the son of a famous local marine architect — G. W. Sivewright's son James P. Sivewright. Another married Dr. Pearson of West Hartlepool).

Donald Barns Morison: Another Scot, born 1859: Served his time at John Elders, Glasgow and after sea service joined Richardsons: at 26 (in 1886) was appointed General Manager after the sudden death of Robert Wyllie. A respected engineer and a considerable innovator who devoted much effort to improvements in boilers, de-aerators, condensers and evaporators, as well as other devices. Invented, inter alia, the Contraflo condenser and suspension furnace, also the "Lock-fast" welded shaft for steamships. With Thomas Richardson (III) he studied use of 3-phase A.C. for driving individual machines in the shops and brought this into the Middleton works in 1899, achieving many orders for the company as a result, and laying the foundation of the later power generating plant work for the Company. In 1900 he was appointed Joint Managing Director of the newly formed Richardsons, Westgarth & Co. Ltd., and later Chairman at Hartlepool on the death of W. J. Richardson. He took much interest in marine oil engine development. Died in Nice on April 30, 1925.

Labour Relations

Whilst this is not intended to be a social history, and the subject of labour relations is not covered in depth, it is one of real importance and no doubt deserves much fuller treatment by some other hand.

The "Herald" of August 1866 reported the Ironmasters were seeking a 10% reduction in wages: the Banking crisis was having serious effect on trade: at this time the collapse of Overend Gurney spelt the end of Pile Spence's Shipyard & Rolling Mills. The crisis had a much wider effect than financial collapses like that — it undermined commercial confidence.

By 1872 there was general acceptance of the long-stated demands of the men for a nine-hour day.

In March of 1874 there was a strike at Richardsons Rolling Mills over the Puddlers not being allowed to "bleed" the iron: this speeded the process but impaired the quality. Orders were scarce so any delay in the restart after the Easter holiday was said not to be a problem for Managers. This period in the 1870's was one of serious recession.

There was a slump in shipbuilding orders in 1884-86, which was hard for the newly created Central Marine Engine Works. In May 1886 Boilermakers' average wage was 33/- per week, after a reduction of 5% to 15%, equal to 2/- per week for skilled men and 1/- for labourers. (The employers said they had been paying more than the district rates — and that rates on the Tyne were much lower. Robert Wyllie was General Manager at this time and a strike of 200-300 men resulted).

In April 1888, the "Herald" reported that both Richardsons and Central Marine had plenty of work. At this time it was said that the CMEW Pattern Makers were paid 30/- to 34/- per week after recent grant of 1/6d — Richardsons men wanted the same.

In July 1888, when CMEW men were out on strike over wages, Richardsons' men agreed to give their recent award of 1/6d per week to CMEW strike fund.

As at July 1891 the pay of Seagoing engineers was stated to be: Med/Black Sea Trades Chief £15 per month or £4.4.0 weekly (vsls above 600 NRT): 2nd Engineer £11 per month or £3.0.0 per week: 3rd Engineer £8 per month or £2.12.0 per week and 4th Engineer £7 per month or £2.7.0 per week.

The Amalgamated Society of Engineers was probably the largest Union in the country in the last third of the 19th Century, and possibly the most powerful, but seem to have been apolitical, even in their great national strike of 1897/98: this was mainly for an eight hour day and caused the employers to band together for the first time in the Engineering Employers' Federation. It lasted from July 1887 to January 1898 and the Mail said that some 3,000 men were out (from Central Marine & Richardsons). Non-union men joined them, but it seems that the boilermakers and pattern makers were not involved, having separate negotiating machinery. There is no doubt that such a prolonged stoppage, including winter months, must have caused great hardship locally.

The press of the period 1866 onwards so often reports wage reductions that it is useful to look at some statistics for the period, as the "Blue Book" of 1903 gives some surprising figures. The movement of 'real' wages 1860 to 1900 was an improvement of 77% — and about one quarter of that in the last 10 years. The change from 1860 to 1890 was some 57%.

At the time of the 1897-8 strike some employers claimed that the men had only had higher pay during the Crimean War of 1854-56.

Finances

Although the family shipbuilding business at Middleton had been forced to close in 1857 after financial difficulties (liabilities in excess of assets to the tune of some £30,000), the engineering side of the Richardson family activities had not been affected and this continued to grow and prosper.

There was a curious but short-lived flirtation with limited liability in September 1865, when Richardsons joined with two shipbuilders to form Richardson, Denton, Duck & Co. Ltd. of Stockton and Hartlepool.

Richardsons was the sole engine works involved in this merger and had by far the largest annual turnover of the three firms involved: £256,000 as against a mere £100,000 for Denton Gray and £140,000 for the Stockton shipbuilders Richardson, Duck & Co., whose owners were Joseph Richardson of 'Woodlands', Stockton and George Nixon Duck of Blue House, Stockton.

Denton Gray built four ships in the name of the consortium and a few T. Richardson engines are shown in Lloyd's Register under that name, with either Stockton or Hartlepool appended, which is misleading. The joint company was broken up 12 months later for reasons probably not unconnected with the banking crisis of 1866, in which the failure of the Overend Gurney Bank brought to an end Pile, Spence & Co. of West Hartlepool, as well as others who banked with them.

The following year Thomas Richardson (II) bought Pile, Spence's Rolling Mills in Mainsforth Terrace, West Hartlepool for £21,677 and set about re-equipping them. At the time he bought them they employed some 500 men, but he soon extended the site from 6 to 12 acres, employing 2,500 and producing weekly 250 tons of plate and 100 tons of rails.

In 1871 Richardson bought the Longhill Estate for £16,000 and on part of it he erected houses for workers at the Mills. The settlement was so remote from the hub of West Hartlepool that it was nicknamed Wagga-Wagga; a name that persists to this day. When the Mainsforth Terrace works was producing steel the tipping of molten slag on the Brenda Road slag-tip produced a red glow in the sky which was locally known as the "Wagga Moon", even after the Second World War. In view of the election pending at the time Richardson acquired the Rolling Mills, the less charitable said he had bought them to roll votes.

In May 1875 the plant was sold to a new Company (West Hartlepool Iron Co. Ltd.), but the financial problems of Thomas Richardson overcame them and they closed down. In 1880 part passed to Carr House Ironworks, and by 1881 the whole was part of the basis of the West Hartlepool Steel & Iron Co.

This acute financial downturn in the Richardson fortunes took place in 1874-5, when a serious general recession, which lasted until 1879, had its effect on Richardsons' engineering work and on the Iron Works they had acquired.

The bombshell dropped at the end of April 1875, when the Herald reported on 30th April:— "Failure announced of Thomas Richardson & Sons". It was estimated that there was some £100,000 due to unsecured creditors, but the nature and reputation of the business was such that the creditors agreed to appoint Robert Fletcher, accountant of Moorgate, London, to carry on the business as Trustee. Thomas Richardson was at that time the Liberal MP for the Hartlepools, but resigned his seat in 1874 in view of his financial problems and the request from the firm's creditors that he devote more time to the business.

The result of these problems was the conversion of the firm into a Limited Liability Company, Thomas Richardson & Son Ltd. That name persisted until the absorption into the larger grouping which became Richardsons Westgarth & Co. Ltd. in 1901.

Machinery, Equipment and Some Notable Achievements

There has already been mention of the introduction of electric light and of electric driving of machinery. Trade paper reviews which came out from time to time were specific about the considerable extent of machine tools and other plant on the Engine Works site, and these comments may be taken to indicate that it was kept well up-to-date, though without an intimate knowledge of the development of machine tools it is not easy to be sure.

During the short existence of Richardson Denton Duck, the Hartlepool works acquired a newly patented locomotive from Leeds builders which the "Herald" of December 1865 headlined as one 'which carries its own water'.

Apart from the successful marine engines produced, and such sought-after products as their improved evaporators, de-aerators and condensers, there were one or two items which rather stand out from local press reports or those in such publications as "The Engineer":—

1888 A new crankshaft (steel) was urgently required for s.s. "Annandale"—the order was received by Richardsons at 11 a.m. Monday and the shaft was completed and despatched by 7 a.m. Friday: a time of 3¾ days. Thomas Richardson's have now made 500 steel crankshafts, reported the South Durham Herald, when commenting on that operation in their issue of 22nd December 1888.

1890 s.s. "Reijnersz": this vessel's original engines were destroyed in a fire while she was building in Holland: Richardsons got the order for a replacement, and her new engines and boilers were made and fitted in eleven weeks from date of order.

The tripling of a number of major ships of the Union Steamship Fleet (mostly "Castle" ships) was considerable feather in Richardsons' cap, as it was done quickly and ingeniously, with very good results.

The Furness Amalgamations
of 1900-1901

Thomas Richardson & Sons Ltd. of Hartlepool, Sir C. Furness, Westgarth & Co. Ltd. of Middlesbrough (formerly Westgarth, English & Co.), and William Allan's Scotia Engine Works of Sunderland were all brought together into Richardsons, Westgarth & Co. Ltd., on the initiative of Sir Christopher Furness of West Hartlepool, Chairman of Furness, Withy and many other companies.

Why, one may ask, did Richardsons stay the course in the marine field, when so many other engine builders came and went, particularly many of the early starters in the field? The Middleton company survived for some 70 years and was prosperous enought in 1900 to form a major unit of the Sir. Christopher Furness' new grouping. There was certainly no lack of competition, and the start of Central Marine in 1883 might be thought to have been a severe threat, especially as Richardsons had no shipyard of their own to create a captive market.

The engine number of the last unit before amalgamation by Furness was around 1085, but of course those numbers included colliery engines, locomotives, pumping machinery and so on, and in any case they probably started at 101. The attached listing of their marine engine output to 1900 may not be complete, but comes to just over 800 ship installations, only very few of which seem to be "boilers only" jobs. This gives an average of about 17 marine engines per annum, but to over 20 per annum if one disregards the very early years. This is not a high figure compared with firms like Blairs of Stockton, but they and others went out of business in the 1930's.

The reasons may well have been that the Richardsons were men of considerable force and foresight, were good "pickers" and gathered around them outstanding and innovative engineers who were encouraged to work up new ideas or improvements on old ideas. They had a workforce of real skills, proud of their work and of the traditions of Richardsons. The expansion of work after installing their own electrical powered machinery is one instance of business acumen in seeing and then serving a new market. They also took up licences, in later years, which allowed them to produce high quality boilers and machinery.

The Group Is Formed

In June 1900 the Press announced that three substantial marine engineering companies were to be amalgamated into a new Group. These were Thomas Richardson & Son Ltd. of Hartlepool Engine Works, Middleton; Sir C. Furness, Westgarth & Co. Ltd. of Middlesbrough, and W. Allan & Co. Ltd. of Scotia Engine Works, Sunderland. Of the three the Hartlepool component was by far the oldest. The first grouping was to change, to wax and wane, as the years passed and within just over sixty years the output of marine machinery had ended at the Hartlepool works.

Richardsons had started building marine engines on the Middleton site in 1851 and the firm's history up to the point when they joined the new grouping has already been covered. After some financial problems in 1874 they had made a recovery and the Middleton business was a sound one in 1900, with an excellent reputation. Furthermore, although marine engines and boilers, together with ancillary equipment (much of it under patents by their own staff) was a very important part of their order books, they had another major string to their bow. The link they had established some years earlier with the Swiss firm of Brown Boveri had led them into making steam-driven power plant for electrical operation of workshop and factory machinery, and their reciprocating engines, with pumps, had been sold to water works, dry-docks and probably other non-marine uses as well.

The Middlesbrough component had a rather different start from the other two firms.

The history of Sir C. Furness, Westgarth & Co., though shorter than that of Richardsons, is more complex. One of the companies chaired by a member of the Pease family (Teeside Iron & Engine Works) was in financial trouble in 1896, and had posted a loss of almost £8000 for the previous year. In March of 1896 the Board proposed to sell out in response to an offer from a syndicate headed by Sir Christopher Furness of West Hartlepool. He was offering to buy the works, together with the engine works of Westgarth, English.

On 11th July 1896 Mr. William Barclay Peat (accountant) announced that the syndicate was to form three companies: —

1. Westgarth, English Tees Furnace Co.: Purchase price £43,000. Improvements to cost £15,000. There were two blast furnaces, producing haematite pig-iron. The first directors to be J. Calder and T. Westgarth, with H. Marshall as Manager.

2. Teesside Bridge & Engineering Co. with a capital £50,000 — to take in the bridge work of the old Teesside, and the marine side of Westgarth. Marine operations would move to Commercial Street, Middlesbrough and the bridge-making to Cargo Fleet Lane, where new plant would be installed. The cost was estimated to be £29,250 plus £10,750 for alterations.

3. Furness, Westgarth & Co. — to be in Commercial Street, Middlesbrough, on the site of the former Copley Turner works, upstream of Dent's Wharf, on the south bank of the Tees, held freehold with a 100-ton sheerlegs installed. This company was based upon the engineering business of Westgarth, English & Co. in which Sir C. Furness had lately gained control. It had been founded in North Ormesby in 1881 (as Westgarth, English) by Tom Westgarth and Harold English. Their production was a varied selection of quite large industrial equipment, including triple expansion steam engines for rolling mills, blast furnace blowers, as well as boilers and gas and other engines for electricity generation. Their first marine engine was probably that installed in the Craggs-built "Hunstanton" in 1882 — a 2-cylinder compound engine with cylinders of 26 and 48 inches and stroke of 36 inches. A number of engines for ships from Craggs shipyard followed. The firm had the sole U.K. rights to manufacture Weiss's Patent Condensers, "largely used in the Ironworks of America and Germany".

In 1891 English had sold out, and the business had been carried on by Tom Westgarth with Craggs, the shipbuilder, as a fairly natural sleeping partner.

(Although the new marine engine business started as 'Furness, Westgarth' it soon had a name change becoming — until the 1900 merger — 'Sir Christopher Furness, Westgarth'. For the year ended 25th August 1900 Sir C. Furness, Westgarth & Co. reported a profit of more than £29,000 with a satisfactory order book and an increased demand for 'Blake' boilers.)

The Sunderland branch of the new Richardsons, Westgarth grouping was the Scotia Engine works of W. Allan & Co. This had been founded in 1887 by a remarkable man — born in Dundee in 1837, William Allan (later to be Sir

RICHARDSONS, WESTGARTH & CO.

LIMITED.

Marine and Electrical Engineers, Boiler Makers, &c. ;

IN WHICH IS INCORPORATED

THOMAS RICHARDSON & SONS, LIMITED, Hartlepool.
SIR CHRISTOPHER FURNESS, WESTGARTH & COMPANY, LIMITED, Middlesbrough.
WILLIAM ALLAN & COMPANY, LIMITED, Sunderland.

INCORPORATED UNDER THE COMPANIES ACTS, 1862 TO 1898.

SHARE CAPITAL - - £700,000,

DIVIDED INTO

350,000 **PREFERENCE SHARES** of £1 each entitled to 6 per cent. Cumulative Preferential Dividend	£350,000
350,000 **ORDINARY SHARES** of £1 each	£350,000
ALSO ,	
4½ PER CENT. PERPETUAL DEBENTURE STOCK	£350,000

This issue provides £200,000 in Cash for working capital and extensions.

Furness, Withy & Co., Limited, have applied in terms of this Prospectus for 50,000 Ordinary Shares, and Shareholders in the amalgamated Companies together with the Directors of this Company have applied in similar terms for 150,000 Preference and 150,000 Ordinary Shares, and for £100,000 Debenture Stock. These applications will be allotted in full. Subject to this condition, the whole of the Share Capital and Debenture Stock is now offered for Subscription at par.

PAYABLE AS FOLLOWS:—	SHARES.		DEBENTURE STOCK.
On Application	£0 2 0		10 per cent.
On Allotment	0 8 0		40 ,,
One Month after Allotment ...	0 10 0		50 ,,

TRUSTEES FOR DEBENTURE STOCK HOLDERS.

SIR RAYLTON DIXON.
HENRY WITHY.
WM. B. PEAT.

DIRECTORS.

SIR CHRISTOPHER FURNESS, M.P., *Chairman.*
SIR THOMAS RICHARDSON, *Vice-Chairman.*
W. J. RICHARDSON.
WILLIAM ALLAN, M.P.
STEPHEN W. FURNESS.
TOM WESTGARTH, } *Managing Directors.*
D. B. MORISON,

LOCAL DIRECTORS.

GEORGE WESTGARTH, Middlesbrough.
ALFRED HARRISON, Sunderland.

BANKERS.

NATIONAL PROVINCIAL BANK OF ENGLAND, LIMITED, Bishopsgate Street, London ; and Branches.

SOLICITORS TO THE TRUSTEES FOR DEBENTURE STOCK HOLDERS.

TURNBULL & TILLY, West Hartlepool.

SOLICITORS TO THE COMPANY.

MUNNS & LONGDEN, 8, Old Jewry, E.C.
JACKSON & JACKSON, Middlesbrough-on-Tees.

BROKERS.

BUCKLER, NORMAN & CRISP, 11, Angel Court, E.C.

AUDITORS.

W. B. PEAT & CO., 3, Lothbury, E.C., and Middlesbrough, Chartered Accountants.

SECRETARY.	ABSISTANT SECRETARY.	REGISTERED OFFICES
HENRY H. MURRAY.	HENRY BARNES.	HARTLEPOOL ENGINE WORKS, Hartlepool

PREFERENCE AND ORDINARY SHARES.

It is intended to pay Dividends on the Preference Shares in May and November.

The Dividend on the Ordinary Shares in each year is limited to 8 per cent. until a Reserve is accumulated of £100,000 intended primarily for the Security of the Preference Shareholders.

The Preference Shares rank as to Dividend and Capital in priority to the Ordinary Shares. The Preference Shareholders have no right of voting on resolutions relating to the general business or administration of the Company. In the event of a voluntary winding up the Preference Shares will rank pro rata with the Ordinary Shares in any surplus after the Capital has been returned to the Shareholders.

PERPETUAL DEBENTURE STOCK.

The Interest is payable half-yearly in January and July.

The Stock (transferable in multiples of £1) will be secured by a Trust Deed constituting a First Mortgage on the Freehold and Leasehold Property of the Company, and a floating charge on its undertaking, exclusive of uncalled Capital, reserving, however, the right of the Company to charge, either by way of floating charge or mortgage, or both, any separate and independent property hereafter acquired. In the event of a voluntary winding-up, the Stock will be paid off at the rate of £110 for each £100 of Stock.

William Allan, M.P.) was taken on as a probationary working engineer ashore after an apprenticeship which started when he was 10 years old, and later he joined the Royal Navy as an engineer, spending some years in that capacity. He transferred to the Merchant service, and was involved in blockade running during the American Civil War, which broke out when he was 24. After capture he was imprisoned by the 'Federals' in the Old Capitol Gaol for some time. It seems likely that the blockade-running had been profitable for him, as it had been for Robert Irvine, West Hartlepool shipbuilder, and many others.

On his return to England, Allan became the forceful and successful Manager of the North Eastern Engine Works, Sunderland, leaving that post in 1887 to set up his own business. This was the Scotia Works, on the south bank of the Wear, formerly the works of Carr & Co. Here William Allan succeeded in getting for his enterprise a fairly good flow of marine engine and boilers orders. He earned a reputation of being a severe critic of Navy engineering — in fact his obituarist in the Northern Daily Mail described him as "a veritable thorn in the flesh of the Secretary of the 'Queen's Navee', speaking with most effect in his condemnation of the Belleville boilers." These attacks earned him, in some quarters, the soubriquet of "Boiler Allan". When asked where he was educated he would reply, it is said, "The world has been my chief educator, and men my books".

Scotia works produced largely triple expansion machinery, but was early in the field with quadruple expansion engines, for lower fuel consumption. Their first design was probably on three cranks, with the extra cylinder — operated by a transverse beam from the crosshead — above the normal H.P. cylinder. This engine suffered mechanical troubles and seems to have been abandoned after the initial batch. In fact the first seven marine engine orders booked in 1888 by Allan were quadruple expansion (Nos. 101-107), with a further quad (No. 116) booked 1889; it is not possible to ascertain the model of engine from the Lloyd's Register entries for these early vessels. Allan was an enthusiastic inventor, and one of his ideas was a "leaping torpedo" which was intended to jump over defensive nets. On trials it jumped over a pier at Sunderland and was thought to be so erratic that the idea was dropped.

William Allan, almost entirely self-educated, was elected to the Commons in 1893 as the Radical Member for Gateshead, and re-elected again in 1895 and 1900. He died in December 1903 at his Sunderland home, Scotland House, leaving five sons, four daughters and several volumes of poetry, much of it in Scots dialect. He is remembered for having been an employer who was very early (at least in the North East) in introducing the eight-hour day: perhaps this stemmed from his boyhood experiences. Another of his advanced ideas was the introduction of 'sandwich courses' for apprentices — six months college and six months in the shops. His belief in hard work was exemplified, it is said, by a carved board at the works entrance which read: "All ye that enter here, row (roll) up your sleeves."

Some Scotia Works Board notes have survived, including those of the time when Sir Christopher Furness was making his bid for the works to bring it into his new engineering combine, and they reveal that competition between engine builders in 1899 and 1900 was severe. Sir Christopher was always a man to drive a keen bargain, whether buying ships, their engines or businesses.

Sir William Allan's company held its last Annual General Meeting on the 11th May 1900, and declared a dividend. It seems probable that by this date Sir C. Furness had decided to acquire the company, and equally probable that Sir William Allan had already made contact with Furness on that subject. At the end of May it was disclosed to the Board that an offer of £60,000 had been received. As Allan was away, the meeting was adjourned until his return. On 8th June Sir William Allan told his fellow directors that Furness would purchase the company "as a going concern (as at 31st March 1900) for £62,250 less 4% for expenses, etc."

He recommended acceptance of this offer "in view of approaching dull times", but there was opposition, and eventually after Furness had been telephoned during the meeting, the 4% deduction was waived and a sale was agreed. The sorting out of detail took some time, of course, but from that point Allans kept Furness well advised of what they were doing, and much of this was through Tom Westgarth. One must assume that Sir Christopher had, by early 1900 or perhaps before then, already made up his mind on the wider grouping which followed. It was, however, the end of October 1900 before Sir Christopher sold Scotia Works to the new Richardsons, Westgarth Group — at a price of £82,500. The Furness Westgarth, William Allan and Thomas Richardsons companies were acquired at a total cost of £790,000. On 27th November 1900 the voluntary liquidation of William Allan & Co. Ltd. was agreed.

The new Group's early entry into control of Scotia Works operations is typified by a note in the Allan records of 11th September 1900:

> "Priestman offered firm (for) a 25" stroke set at £9600. Westgarth will agree but wants Morison approval. Says 'price below what we are quoting': estimated cost £8600. Priestman has booked two with George Clark for less.'

At a very early stage (on 2nd November 1900) after inclusion in the Group the Scotia Works directors were recorded as seeking outside approval for the purchase of boiler plates from Beardmores at £9.76 per ton (ready flanged). This may well have been because Furness had been pressing them to buy from his own steel-making interests, which did not supply such plate ready flanged: it appears to have been normal practice for Scotia Works to take in their boiler-plate ready flanged.

After numerous rather complex transactions the position was that by the end of November 1900 all the necessary steps had been taken for the new Group of Richardsons, Westgarth & Co. Ltd. to forge ahead, under the control of

D. B. Morison (Hartlepool) and Tom Westgarth (Middlesbrough), the two joint Managing Directors (each on a seven year contract), who were answerable to the new Board and to Sir Christopher in particular. Tom Westgarth resigned as joint Managing Director in July of 1912, though he remained on the Board; thus Morison became sole Group Managing Director. The Middlesbrough works was (by 1912) under the control of E. Hall-Brown as General Manager. The initial local (Hartlepool) Chairman was William J. Richardson, who retired some time after 1910, when Morison took over the chairmanship at the Hartlepool works. The career of the inventive and energetic Donald Barns Morison is mentioned in Chapter 8. He had by 1900 already been 12 years as General Manager of Hartlepool Engine Works, as successor there to Robert Wyllie. Tom Westgarth was an enlightened employer who was well-respected within the industry: in 1924-5 he was President of the North East Coast Insititution of Engineers and Shipbuilders, and he died in 1934.

The press release of 30th October 1900 on the new combination (issued at the A.G.M. of Sir C. Furness, Westgarth & Co. Ltd., Middlesbrough) reported the main Board officers as: — Chairman, Sir Christopher Furness: Vice-chair, Sir Thomas Richardson: other Directors W. F. Richardson (sic — actually W. J. Richardson), Sir William Allan, M.P., Stephen W. Furness, Tom Westgarth and D. B. Morison, plus George Westgarth as local director at Middlesbrough, and Alfred Harrison as local director at Sunderland. The machinery, tools, etc., had been valued by George Macfarland of Glasgow, consulting engineer, and Joseph Potts, architect of Sunderland, had valued the land and buildings. The total valuation for land, buildings, plant, tools, patterns, etc., plus work in progress, stores, raw materials and Morison's patents was £707,600. Adding the £200,000 working capital in cash which was to come from the flotation meant that there was over £907,000 available as security for the proposed Debenture Stock. Profits of the three constituent companies from 25th August 1900 would accrue to the new Group, and arrangements had been made for the purchase of 'all the patterns (patents?) for the marine specialities of Mr. D. B. Morison'. These included his 'Lock-fast' patents and trade-mark, also future patents, and earned Morison the sum of £60,000 in a separate agreement, the current patents having been examined and approved by Tom Westgarth. W. B. Peat certified that the aggregate profits of the three operating companies for the year 1899-1900 would be £83,283 — after Preference Dividend, Debenture Interest, and £2,500 Director' Fees was paid, this would leave £44,033 for Depreciation, Reserve and Dividend on the Ordinary Shares.

The formal Prospectus & Contract details for the flotation of Richardsons, Westgarth & Co. Ltd. (of which D. B. Morison's personal copy has survived) was issued 2nd November 1900; the Share Capital to be £700,000 of which half in Preference Shares of £1 each and half in Ordinary Shares of £1 each. In addition there was to be an issue of £350,000 of 4½% Perpetual Debenture Stock. Furness, Withy had applied for 50,000 Ordinary Shares, and "shareholders in the amalgamating Companies together with the Directors of this Company have applied in similar terms for 150,000 Ordinary and 150,000 Preference Shares, and for £100,000 Debenture Stock". The remaining shares and stock were offered at par. The Prospectus stated "This issue provides £200,000 in Cash for working capital and extensions", and explained that the union of the three Companies "will result in a more close alliance with the Shipbuilding industry carried on at Hartlepool by Furness, Withy & Co. and Irvine's Shipbuilding & Dry Docks Co., and the Company will, in consequence, secure important orders for Marine Engines from these firms, to mutual advantage".

The Prospectus explained proposals to "transfer the manufacture of some of the subsidiary businesses from the Middlesbrough and Sunderland Works to Hartlepool, and, in connection therewith to make extensions...in the Iron and Brass Foundries, the Forge, the Electrical and Boiler Shops at Hartlepool, and to build a Shop for Specialities, which will result in a considerable increase of the output of the combined works, and in greater economy in production." This change would release space at Sunderland and Middlesbrough for development of the engine trade, and proposed that £100,000 of the issue proceeds be devoted to these developments.

Henry H. Murray was Company Secretary, with Henry Barnes as Assistant Secretary, and the Registered Office of Richardsons, Westgarth & Co. Ltd. was Hartlepool Engine Works.

The Trustees for the Debenture Stock were Sir Raylton Dixon, Henry Withy and William Barclay Peat—three names which would certainly have inspired confidence in potential subscribers to the issue. Solicitors to those Trustees were Turnbull & Tilly of West Hartlepool.

Shipbuilding Links

In 1884, when Edward Withy, shipbuilder at Middleton since 1869, had decided to emigrate to New Zealand, his interest in the shipyard had been taken up by Christopher Furness, and when the London and Hartlepool Furness companies were merged into one organisation in 1891 by the creaton of Furness, Withy & Co. Ltd., it was the Middleton shipyard which supplied the Withy component of the name.

During 1896-7 Furness, Withy had obtained a controlling interest in another West Hartlepool shipyard—that of Robert Irvine which did repair work as well as shipbuilding in West Harbour. Irvine's yard was modernised in 1897 by local contractor Joseph Howe to allow the construction of larger vessels: this may have been at the instigation of Furness, or the need for more capital may have been the spur to get Furness involved in the business. In 1898 Sir Christopher had enlarged the Furness, Withy shipbuilding connection by taking a controlling interest in the Northumberland Shipbuilding Co. of Howden on Tyne, newly created from the Edwards' yard by Rowland Hodge, formerly of C. S. Swan, Hunter & Co. of Wallsend. At least one newspaper report credited Furness with a financial interest in the Norwegian shipyards of Fevig, and the fact that over 40 ships from their two yards (from 1898 to 1909) were engined by the Middlesbrough works supports belief in that report.

By the second half of the nineties the Furness, Withy companies owned or managed a large number of steamers, and were ordering newbuildings on a major scale. Orders for engines would generally be placed by the shipbuilder, unless the shipowner had any particular preference for a make of machinery. Thus Furness, Withy's ownership of three shipyards, and their ability to build tonnage for their own fleet in these yards and elsewhere, made them major players in the ordering of machinery, and it would have seemed important to Furness not to be dependent upon the open market for machinery. With this position in mind, and thinking of the grouping to come, it is of interest to look at where engines were sourced for all the ships built in the two local (Furness-owned) shipyards alone from 1896 to 1899. In addition, the numerous Furness shipowning companies were also ordering newbuildings from other yards not in the Company's ownership during this period.

1896-98 (Irvine's yard was more or less out of commission in 1897)

	TR	WA	WE	FW	B	CM	NEM
Withy	6	5	1	2	2	1	1
Irvine	2	1	-	-	1	1	-

1899

	TR	WA	WE	FW	B	CM	NEM
Withy	3	-	-	5	-	-	-
Irvine	2	1	-	1	-	1	-

(Key to initials: TR-T. Richardson: WA-William Allan: WE-Westgarth, English: FW-Furness, Westgarth: B-Blairs: CM-Central Marine: NEM-North Eastern Marine).

From 1901 almost all the engines for steamers built in these yards came from the three initial members of the new Richardsons Westgarth Group. As Furness Withy had interests which included coal and steel as well as a large fleet of ships, with shipyards and engine works, it would seem that vertical integration was the name of the game at this time. The Hebburn yard of Palmers was an early and perhaps extreme example of that trend: iron ore, coal and limestone arrived at one end of the process, and ships emerged from the other.

The Northumberland Shipbuilding Co. placed a steady flow of engine orders to the Sunderland Works, while the Hartlepool yards mostly favoured the Hartlepool works: later still orders went to the Middlesbrough and Hartlepool works from the Haverton Hill yard of Furness Shipbuilding, when they started production at the end of the first World War.

Page 35

The Growth of Marine Output

The new engineering company grouping made an excellent start, and their press release of December 1901 is headed "The World's Record" (for a single firm's machinery output) and lists 54 ships engined in the year. The total IHP is shown as over 120,000 including electrical generating engines, pumping engines and boilers for marine and land use. The output of "Blake Patent Boilers" alone is given as equivalent to 7,000 IHP. This was, of course, the combined output of three works which had, not long before, been entirely separate. Unfortunately for the historian, the lists of output do not, after 1900, show which of the three component works of the group was responsible for each item.

The two Furness-owned shipyards in The Hartlepools made losses in the recession of the early 1920's, and finally closed in 1924: s.s. 'Heworth' (Yard No. 616) was the last vessel built, and she was engined by North Eastern Marine, which was later to be yet another engine-works included in the RW Group.

The Hartlepool works of Richardsons, Westgarth was under Donald Barns Morison, a Scottish-born engineer of great ability and an inventive turn of mind. His inventions covered all forms of marine engine equipment, but in particular such auxiliaries as evaporators, condensers and feed-heaters. Morison was a pioneer in the use of exhaust steam for heating boiler feed water, and his designs were attractive to other engine-builders and to ship-owners. About 1912 he came to an agreement with Richardsons, Westgarth which allowed him to set up a new company (The Contraflo Condenser & Kinetic Air Pump Co. Ltd.) to market his designs, create new ones and pursue technical development of them. Richardsons, Westgarth and Vickers took up licences to manufacture Contraflo products. Harry Fothergill was a later Director of that company.

The press of 1900 reported a speech by D. B. Morison deploring and criticising "the lack of engine-room skills" in the Royal Navy.

At Hartlepool works the marine machinery was installed in ships either at what later became 'Irvine's Quay', where there was a 70 ton Fairbairn goose-neck crane, or at the 1896 hydraulic sheer-legs on the south side of the North basin, immediately across the basin from the Central Marine Engine Works of William Gray & Co. In later days there were problems with the braking mechanism of the sheer-legs hoist, and many RW fitters lost portions of fingers during the final inching of the engines or boilers into position during the installation of machinery there.

Early Turbines, Marine and Land

By 1903 it was apparent, after Parsons' demonstrations, that the turbine was becoming increasingly popular as a motive unit for ships and for land use, and the Group decided it should meet this demand. A new turbine shop was erected as an extension of the Hartlepool works on the south side of Princess Street, Middleton, to the south of the relatively new main offices there. The Brown-Boveri type of turbine was produced — Thomas Richardson & Sons had entered into an agreement with the Swiss firm 1897 as regards electrical generating plant, and this was extended to the prime mover turbines. During the first year of production five modest sized turbine-driven electrical generators were produced, the largest being one of 750 kW for Cargo Fleet Iron Co. (a Furness Company).

However, the main business of the Hartlepool works from 1900 until after the first World War was the building of triple and quadruple expansion steam engines, with their boilers and associated plant. Some notable engines were produced: William E. Loveridge, a later Managing Director, instances in his paper on the works history the following: —

s.s. "Riverina" (J. Laing 1905) — a triple of 32", 51" and 84" x 54" stroke. 4650 IHP. Eng. No. 1187. Owners: Huddart Parker Line.

s.s. "El Paraguaya" and "La Correntina" (Irvine's 1912) — twin screw engines of 5,900 IHP for refrigerated vessels for Furness-Withy companies. Engine Nos. 1286 & 1298.

s.s. "Oosterdijk" and "Westerdijk" (Irvine's 1913) — quadruple expansion engines of 27.5", 37.75", 55", 84" x 60" stroke. Engine Nos. 1307 & 1308. For the Holland-Amerika Line.

When RW engined the Furness-Withy built steam tanker "Beaumont/Seminole" in 1902 the oil-burning boilers were fitted with the 'Flannery-Boyd system' of oil-firing, according to the Northern Daily Mail of December that year.

There was a steady intake of apprentices, and one whose indentures have survived from 1910 was George Lines of Hartlepool, indentured for five years as an Apprentice Fitter; his weekly rate of pay started at 5 shillings, rising to 11 shillings per week in 1914, his final year. The Company's seal was affirmed by W. J. Richardson & Henry Murray, Directors and by Henry Barnes, Company Secretary, and completion of the Indenture was certified by E. Thomas, Works Manager. The rates of pay for apprentices were fairly standard throughout the industry.

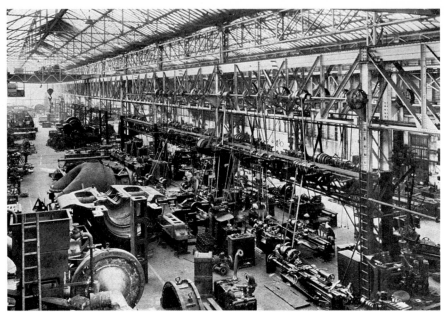

HARTLEPOOL WORKS—TURBINE SHOP.

First British-built and owned ocean-going merchant ship to be propelled by an oil engine was the 1,800-ton "Eavestone" of 1912.

Marine Diesel Ventures

The Marine Diesel had made its practical debut in 1912, when Burmeister & Wain fitted a four-stroke engine into m.v. "Selandia". That same year the Belgian firm of Carel Freres had developed a design and Richardsons, Westgarth took up a licence from the Belgians to build their diesels; this task was initially assigned to their Middlesbrough Works, which had experience in building gas engines for land use. They produced one of 800 BHP which was fitted into the Tees-built and Furness-owned "Eavestone". The Carel Freres design was a two-stroke engine, with four cylinders of 20 inches diameter and a stroke of 36 inches. The cylinders, valves and camshaft gearing came from Ghent — the remainder of the engine was made by RW. Cooling of pistons, liners, heads, guide-pins and main bearings was by sea-water. Fuel was air-injected, and the exhaust gases were led up a derrick post on the bridge deck — the funnel merely served the two donkey boilers which were installed. The compact nature of the power unit and fuel storage, compared with a steam reciprocating engine and coal-burning boilers, allowed additional capacity for cargo — this was estimated at 400 tons for the "Eavestone"; clearly a merit point with shipowners.

A new engine usually has teething troubles, and this was indeed no exception. There were problems with liners and pistons; the ship suffered serious engine problems in 1913 and spent some time in the Azores waiting for spares to reach her there. It was unfortunate that the progress of remedial work on the engine was interrupted by the outbreak of war in 1914, as it meant that the considerable sums expended by RW on development were more or less wasted. In view of the need for reliability in wartime the "Eavestone" was re-engined with a triple expansion set, and no more Carel Freres engines were built by Richardsons, Westgarth.

The First World War
(1914-18)

After the outbreak of the first World War the works' priority was to complete the private contracts which were well advanced, and at the same time somehow find spare capacity for essential Admiralty work. Some shipyards had taken orders for delivery in 1914 at a premium price, and it was commercially important that these be completed. The first naval contracts were for Patrol vessels being built in the Tees by the W. Harkess yard; twin screw turbine vessels of 3,500 SHP. (Engine Nos. 2341, 2352, 2382). Other naval work followed, notably sets of triples on four cranks for Flower Class Sloops being constructed in various North East shipyards. (Engine Nos. 2342-45, 2349-50, 2374, 2381,2383-4). These triple expansion engines, of 2700 IHP, had four cylinders — 22, 35, 40 and 40 inches diameter, with a stroke of 30 inches. Steam at 180 p.s.i.g. was supplied by two boilers of 16 feet diameter. Two large sets of geared turbines, each 27,000 SHP, were supplied for Sunderland-built Destroyers from the Doxford shipyard (HMS "Vega" and "Velox", Engine Nos. 2372 & 2373), and a number of high-output triples sets for Admiralty oil tankers, such as Engine No. 2352 (for "Slavol"), which was a triple of 3375 IHP, with cylinders of 26", 42.5" & 70" x 45" stroke; steam pressure was 200 p.s.i.g. and the propeller shaft speed 96 rpm.

Ship losses due to U-boat attack during the War, particularly in 1916-17, resulted in the overdue initiation of an intensive Admiralty programme of building of standard vessels, and the Hartlepool works supplied a considerable number of triple sets for Merchant Ship Types "A", "B" and "C", from various yards. These engines were mainly in two sizes: —

25", 41" and 68" x 45" stroke (2300 IHP) and

27", 44" and 73" x 48" stroke (2700 IHP).

and are typified by engines Nos. 2387 and 2388.

Loveridge states that between 1903 and 1918, 127 turbine sets were built at Hartlepool, of which 45 were Curtis-type and the remainder Impulse Reaction type. Most of these were for electrical generating, but seven marine units for the Admiralty are included in the total. The report "Work of the Principal Industries of the North East Coast during the 1914-1918 War" reports that the combined output of the three Richardsons, Westgarth establishments comprised: —

> "the engining of 146 vessels of the following classes: — Destroyers, Patrol Boats, Oil Tankers, Mine Sweepers, Monitors, Sloops, Ice-Breakers, Meat Carriers, Cargo Boats, Standard Ships and Trawlers — Total Horsepower 502,960."

Unfortunately, as order book dates are not always clear, it is difficult to separate out the production of each of the three works, but the list of Hartlepool engines forming an Appendix to this history gives a basis for assessment of Hartlepool's contribution to that total. The author's research has discovered one oddity in the 1917 production — the Hartlepool Works' order book shows six small triples (Nos. 2375-2380) supplied to 'Mersey' Class armed trawlers built by Cochranes of Selby:

the builders' yard books credit C. D. Holmes of Hull with the engines for all six of these small vessels. The probable explanation is that RW (Hartlepool) were sub-contractors to Holmes for these engines.

Condensing plants, mostly of the Morison patent 'Contraflo' type, for marine and land use produced during the same period numbered 147, in a range from a few square feet of cooling surface to one of 40,000 square feet for Manchester Corporation. This last was to operate with a 25,000 kW turbine set supplied by Richardsons, Westgarth of Hartlepool for driving the City's new electrical generating plant. There is some irony in the fact that the head of Manchester Corporation's Electricity Department (Mr. S. L. Pearce) had served an apprenticeship with Central Marine Engine Works. When it was commissioned there was the usual demonstration of smooth running by means of a florin standing on edge on the turbine casing, and the press made much of the "50 million gallons of water per day passing through the 30 miles of brass tubing in the condenser".

From 1918 to 1938: Triples, Turbines and Diesels

Once the war had ended there was an initial rush of orders for ships to replace those lost by submarine and other causes, and the main demand on the Marine Department was for steam reciprocating machinery. By now superheated steam was well established in use, and poppet valves were being fitted to the H.P. cylinder. Some geared turbine sets were also produced, these being for liner vessels requiring speed above that of the normal tramp steamer, prinicipally ordered by Furness Withy companies.

The works order book for 1920 has rather cryptic entries against engine order numbers 2610 and 2611 — "Engines supplied by C.G.M.S.". The likely meaning of this is "Central Government Machinery Store", which held a number of 'surplus' war production marine engines — engines produced for hulls ordered by the Ministry which were never built during the emergency: engine production had outstripped the output of the shipyards. A number of such engines were advertised for sale in the shipping periodicals of 1920-21.

Beardmore-Tosi Diesels

The management had not lost sight of the potential business which lay in the marine diesel engine, although its development had been more or less halted by the needs of the war. Furness, Withy decided that two of a series of 6,000 ton deadweight vessels building in 1922-24 for their companies should be diesel-engined. After research and enquiries the choice fell on an Italian design and an agreement was made with Franco Tosi of Legnano to build that design under licence, jointly with William Beardmore of Glasgow, who were by then already building these Italian engines, which were of the four-stroke blast injection type. The two chosen vessels for this trial were "Sycamore" (1923) and "Tramore" (1924), which were built as "Brazilian Prince" and "Castilian Prince" — both from Furness Shipbuilding at Haverton Hill, of 3907 gross tons.

It must be said that the Tosi engine was not a success — it was reported to be mechanically sound, but it had a poor power-to-weight ratio and was expensive to produce. Lawrence Walker (an apprentice from 1925 to 1930), who worked on these engines, recalls that the cylinder covers gave a great deal of trouble.

Morison served with energy and distinction on an industry committee on diesel propulsion, and it seems probable that more than one of the Furness companies was helpful in the research into performance and development. This is exemplified by the fact that "Sycamore" was put at the disposal of the Marine Oil Engine Trials Committee, which was chaired by Morison. It will have been noted that the first Tosi diesel engines from RW were for ships owned by Furness companies, and the cost to those who made material contributions must have been very substantial. The death of D.B. Morison in 1925 was a serious loss to the Group, and probably to the drive to develop greater diesel expertise. The Company set up in his memory the D.B. Morison Scholarship for Apprentices, which was competed for annually.

After Morison's death the management of the Marine side was in the hands of William E. Loveridge, and the Land work was controlled by Moritz G.S. Swallow. George Clark became Managing Director — a man remembered for his habit of whistling as he left his office to make his rounds of the works: perhaps as a warning of his impending arrival.

Doxford Engines

At this time the Sunderland firm of Doxford had been active in developing an opposed-piston two-stroke type of marine diesel: their first commercial units were installed in two ships for Scandinavian owners ("Eknaren" and "Ingaren"). The Board of R.W. thought that this Doxford product showed potential, as it seemed to be reliable and reasonable in cost. The Hartlepool works became (in 1924 or 1925) the first firm to be licensed by Doxfords for the manufacture of their new diesel.

A new erecting shop was put up for building Doxfords at Hartlepool, with space for six engines to be built at a time: the completion of the shop was somewhat delayed by the 1926 General Strike, during which all the work-people were 'out', but not, of course, the apprentices, whose indentures precluded them from striking. They were not allowed to do any productive work during the strike, but found ways in which to occupy themselves.

It must have been an impressive sight to see a number of engines in that shop in various stages of construction. When one or more engines was running in the shop on test the noise was tremendous, and once they were on full power trials there were few gas-mantles in the houses of Middleton which could survive the vibration.

In 1927 and 1928 Hartlepool completed their first three engines of this pattern, each of 2,500 BHP, for ships of the British Tanker Company fleet — "British Renown" (Engine No. 2659), "British Freedom" (2666) and "British Justice" (2667). The "British Renown" was in service for some 30 years, which reflects great credit on the design and the build-quality of the engine. It has been claimed that the Hartlepool-built Doxfords were the best constructed of any made by licensees of the engine; some have gone so far as to assert that they were better than those from Doxfords' own works. Two further RW-Doxford engines were built at the Group's Middlesbrough works for the "Gulf Wing" and "Gulf Hawk", probably in 1928.

The Decline of the Sunderland & Middlesbrough Works

By 1927 there were clear signs that the Hartlepool works had become the major element in the group, as the press release of December 1927 showed outputs for the year to have been: —

Hartlepool works 28,440 IHP

Middlesbrough works 5,050 IHP (This output was probably all non-marine, as the author has not traced any marine engine production between 1923 and the few later RW-Doxfords of 1928-29).

Sunderland works 6,800 IHP (This works was to cease engine production in 1929).

The steamer "Pilar" (ex "London Queen" of 1910, for a Dutch yard) is a good advertisement for the build quality of the steam engines from the Middlesbrough works: Lloyds Register of 1991 shows this vessel still in class and in service with her original 1910 triple. The Middlesbrough operation seems to have produced over 380 marine engine sets before it ended — this total includes Westgarth, English and Furness, Westgarth production.

Home-grown Diesel Technology: The "Burn" Engines

The attractions of the diesel to the shipowner included fuel economy and the smaller engine-room staff needed, although the initial cost was considerably higher than for a steam reciprocating installation of similar output. A number of shipowners were turning to this new propulsive unit, and it became clear that the day of the diesel was coming. D.B. Morison therefore decided that time and money should be devoted in trying to develop a marine diesel engine with a better power-to-weight ratio than was usual, and which would cost less per BHP than existing designs. The direction he chose was the two-stroke engine. This design and development work was delegated to Walter Scott Burn, M.Sc., who had joined RW soon after the War in connection with the Tosi engine. His remit, given in 1924, was to create a design on the chosen lines, and to incorporate whatever improvements were known at that time. The final design was a two-stroke airless injection engine, with twin horizontal scavenge pumps gear-driven from the main crankshaft, and a cam-operated fuel injection system. This was at a time when other engine makers were pinning their faith on the four-stroke cycle, whereas Richardsons had foreseen that the logical line of advance for the marine diesel would be the double-acting two-stroke. Later events were to prove that choice to have been correct in one respect—the two-stroke cycle.

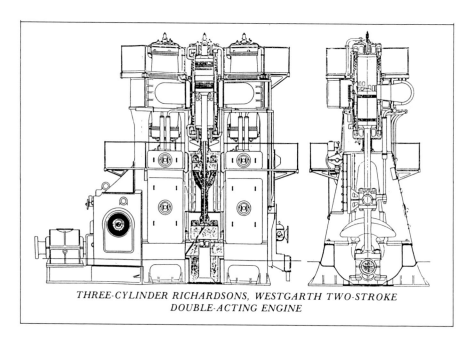

THREE-CYLINDER RICHARDSONS, WESTGARTH TWO-STROKE DOUBLE-ACTING ENGINE

The first Burn prototype, given the number H3000, was built as a two-cylinder unit, and underwent exhaustive testing: only one of the cylinders was fitted with running gear, the other being a "dummy". Continuous running for a long period was part of the testing programme, and it is said that the engine would have run continuously for much longer had it not stopped after 30 days by reason of a burst fuel pipe. The engine was rated at 1,000 BHP per cylinder, and had many novel and advanced features, including interchangeable cylinder covers; it was completed for start-up in April 1926.

The first commercial engine of the type (Engine No. H3001) was taken up by the brave shipowner Sir John Esplen for a tanker of 3,200 tons deadweight, m.v. "Irania", built in 1929 by the Blythswood yard of Glasgow. It was rather smaller than H3000, being a three cylinder unit with an output of 1,250 BHP, and was in fact the **all-British** double-acting two stroke oil engine to operate at sea. Some mechanical problems occurred in service with pistons and with cylinder covers, and the fuel consumption was not as good as had been predicted, so further orders were, unfortunately, not immediately forthcoming. It was an engine which had been closely watched by the marine engineering world, and was described in some detail in an article in "Syren & Shipping" of 1st January 1930. Others, too, showed interest in the Burn engine. The "Irania", quite early in her service, is said to have taken bunker fuel to Kiel for the German Navy, and a story is told of several local "gentlemen in smart blazers" coming aboard to look round the vessel — these visitors were taken to be thinly disguised officers of the German Navy.

A story is related by Fred Taylor and some others about the "Irania" diesel installation. When the ship's trials were completed after a re-fit, Mr. Burn told the Chief Engineer that at 105 rpm he would have no worries. However, either Mr. Albert Leeson, RW's Diesel Manager, or (more probably) RW's Guarantee Engineer, Mr. Wilfred Gardner — versions differ — was present and went on to ask the Chief if he like an undisturbed night's sleep at sea. "Of course", was the reply. "In that case", said Mr. Gardner (or Mr. Leeson), "stick to 95 rpm, Chief, and you'll get your nights in bed." What, if anything, Mr. Walter Burn said is not recorded!

The "Syren" report says that the "Irania" engine (No. H3001) was made with "no departure of note from the general principles of the original design". The ship had a chequered career. At one time she was brought round from Liverpool to Hartlepool, for possible sale after a refit, and RW personnel manned the engines for that trip. There were two breakdowns on the voyage — one was in the scavenge pump, but the other was in a Polar diesel generator which suffered a fire in the exhaust system. The vessel's steering gear and navigation lights failed when the generator went down and passing London-bound colliers bombarded the ship with a great deal of abuse.

Burn diesel engine No. H3002 was built for land use — a four cylinder 1,000 BHP engine for Ashford Power Station. Tests showed that it was not able to produce the output required by the clients, and they rejected it. The engine was stored at the Hartlepool works pending a decision on its future, and some years later (in 1937) it was modified, fitted with reversing gear, and installed in a cargo ship, "Saint Germain", to replace her existing machinery. The Lloyd's Register entry for the "Saint Germain" shows the engine as having been built in 1930, installed in 1937. Again there was difficulty in reaching the rated output, and the Burn engine was eventually replaced by RW at their expense.

Burn engines Nos. H3003 and H3004, four cylinder units designed for an output of 4,000 BHP at 105 rpm, were fitted in two vessels for the Silver Line ("Silverpine" and "Silverlarch"). The guaranteed fuel consumption was not reached, but the rated output was achieved. There were all too frequent breakdowns at sea, and the cost to RW must have been very high indeed. These ships had been built in 1924 on the Tyne, and fitted originally with 2,000 HP Neptune diesel engines, giving a 10 knot service speed. Stanley & John Thompson, the managers of the Silver Line, had decided in 1934 to modernise these two ships and improve their speed, as 10 knots was no longer adequate. The decision to fit a new engine and propeller to achieve over 13 knots necessitated re-shaping the stern — an intricate task carried out perfectly by Joseph L. Thompson's yard at Sunderland. After that the vessels came to Hartlepool where the RW double-acting airless injection engines were fitted — cylinder diameter was 27.5 inches, and stroke 47.5 inches. Bedplates and columns were of welded construction, and the design speed of the modernised ships was 13.5 knots at 109 revolutions. The magazine "Motor Ship" of March 1935 carried an article on the conversion of these two ships, which spent some time under the North Basin sheerlegs at Hartlepool while their new machinery was being installed.

The author has had the benefit of discussing these engines with Lawrence Walker, who worked on them as an apprentice and later (after some sea-time) for a brief period as a fitter. He chose to take the 'Burn' engine as the subject for his paper submitted in the D.B. Morison Scholarship examination, and he made some critical remarks about the engine — which may explain why he was second in the contest. Now long retired after a distinguished career as a Chief Engineer with British Tankers, but with vivid memories of his apprenticeship, he still holds to his original view that some of the components were too heavy, and that Richardsons started rather late in the day on the development of their own marine diesel engine, when a number of others were already further down the road of marine diesel development.

Walter Burn was later to move to London, where he worked as a Consultant on a wide range of projects, including torpedo design, and from time to time was in contact with Richardsons, Westgarth.

Curiously none of these Burn engines appear in the works order book, but they have been added to the listing of engine output apprended to this history.

Further RW-Doxford Engines

Further Doxford engines were built and installed in 1929, 1930 and 1931.

RW-Doxford engines were chosen for three twin screw liner vessels built by J.L. Thompson of Sunderland in 1929-30 ("Silverpalm" and "Silverwillow" — Engine Nos. 2674/5). "Silveryew" was also given similar engines in 1930, this pair of engines having been built in RW's Middlesbrough works, under Albert Leeson, with assistance from some of the Hartlepool personnel. Further Hartlepool-built Doxfords went into two Furness ships built on the Clyde at the Blythswood yard in 1929 ("Cingalese Prince" and "Siamese Prince" — Engine Nos. 2671/2), and another into the tanker "British Strength" (Engine No. 2676). All these were 4 cylinder engines with 600mm cylinders x 1800mm combined stroke, developing 6000 total BHP.

After that the next RW-Doxfords went into "Port St. John" in 1938 (engine No. 2685), and "St. Essylt" in 1941 (Engine No. 2695), both single screw vessels. The time gap between these engines cause by the crankshaft for the second having been ordered originally from the Czech company Skoda. When the Germans marched into Czechoslovakia a new crankshaft was ordered in Belgium, but the German invasion of the Netherlands meant that one was never received, either. Eventually a crankshaft was obtained from British sources and the engine was completed. The ship's trial trip was in September 1941. Bill Summers, an apprentice at the time, well remembers the moment when the engine was started up in the shop after assembly with the long-awaited crankshaft; feral pigeons had taken to nesting in the shop exhaust system during the engine's long dormant period, and Middleton village was subjected to a 'veritable blizzard' of pigeon nests and feathers as the long idle RW-Doxford came to life.

The Trade Depression of 1931-37

These were years in which few ships were built (in two of them Wm. Gray of West Hartlepool did not launch one vessel), and as a result engine prices tumbled. One sad result was that the Middlesbrough Works of Richardsons, Westgarth closed — some of the key personnel transferred to Hartlepool, including Mr. Albert Leeson, Diesel Manager from the Middlesbrough plant. Scotia Works had built its last marine engine in January 1929, having produced about 320 marine engines. The works continued in the group with minor work until 1946, when the site was sold to S.P. Austin & Co. When engine production fell off at Sunderland a number of skilled people came to Hartlepool, including Charles Frank, who retired in

1954 from Hartlepool works after over fifty years in the marine engineering industry; he had served an apprenticeship at Central Marine Engine Works. Charles Frank's son Reg had, in his time, been an apprentice at the Hartlepool Works of Richardsons, Westgarth.

The Foster-Wheeler Connection

RW sought any kind of engineering work to keep the establishment going during the slump, and had some success in securing orders for a range of general engineering products. Included in these were orders from an American company, newly located in the London area, for oil refinery equipment such as heat exchangers. These orders were the beginning of a long and valuable association with the Foster-Wheeler Corporation, leading to RW taking up a licence to build the Foster-Wheeler design of boilers and economisers for land and marine use. This licence, in fact, seems to have been the key to RW obtaining substantial orders for land-use water-tube boilers, even in the face of competition from other boiler makers long established in that field.

Such work was sorely needed, as the order book shows no marine engines ordered between 1931 (No. 2678) for "Svend Foyn" and 1936 (No. 2679) for "Syrian Prince" — a Furness Liner vessel.

The Company had for many years been building its own type of "Nesdrum" water-tube boilers for land and marine use, but the lower demand for this type of boiler and the excellence of the American design was such that the FW boilers, with FW economisers, soon became the major item in the Hartlepool boiler shops. Other works in the group had ample capacity for building the traditional Scotch boilers and "Nesdrum" water-tube boilers, so those lines of production were dropped in the Hartlepool boiler shop. The steam and water drums for the FW boilers were bought in by Hartlepool Works and not manufactured locally.

As the boiler was of a very different design from the usual multi-tubular marine boiler, a training installation was set up at Hartlepool Works to instruct marine engineers in the correct style of boiler management and maintenance for Foster-Wheeler water-tube boilers.

Meanwhile, in 1938, Richardsons, Westgarth had undergone radical changes. It had become the parent company for a Group consisting of the following three operating companies: —

Richardsons, Westgarth (Hartlepool) Ltd., whose earlier history has already been outlined.

George Clark (1938) Ltd., formed from an engineering firm established in Sunderland in 1848, which had produced its first marine engine in 1854.

North Eastern Marine Engineering (1938), which had started in Sunderland in 1865, expanding to an additional works at Wallsend in 1882.

In 1940 a further acquisition was made — this was John Dickinson & Sons, Ltd. of Sunderland — engine builders founded in 1852 and still under the control of the Dickinson family until the sale to the RW Group.

This merger brought in some notable engineering personalities to the Group; men such as O.J. Philipson and Max Woosnam of N.E.M. The latter was a tennis Gold & Silver Medallist at the Antwerp Olympics of 1920, and had numerous other sporting achievements to his credit. From this time the character of the Group changed, and overall control of the Hartlepool Works was mainly by men who were described in Hartlepool as "Wallsend people", which does not seem to have been a compliment, in spite of the undoubted ability and enterprise of most of them. One former employee described the changes after N.E.M. joined as "an invasion of directors from Wallsend — a sort of musical chairs". Others suggest this is somewhat unfair, as the Group was controlled by the Group Board in Wallsend, and it was the Group Board which had the responsibility for the hiring and firing of senior management people.

Recovery and the War of 1939-45

The approach of World War II had its effect on the freight markets and the demand for tonnage; engine orders began to flow in. The slump in trade had so reduced orders for new tonnage from the shipyards that in 1938 the British Government offered a modest subsidy to shipowners as an inducement to them to build new vessels and so give some help to those heavy industrial areas which had suffered so much. It was fortunate that this "scrap & build" spur to the shipbuilding and engineering industry led to some regeneration of industrial capacity which was to prove very valuable at the start of the second World War.

Thus after a gap of years the Company had begun to build triples again, and in 1937 had received an order of two sets of single reduction geared turbines for a couple of twin screw warships built at Devonport (HM Ships "Leda" and "Seagull"): designed for a propeller shaft speed of 275 rpm. (Engines 2683-4). Further Admiralty orders came in 1941 for turbine sets of 4,300 BHP in the twin screw ships HMS "Erne" and "Ibis" — in these two vessels the boilers were supplied by Hawthorn, Leslie on the Tyne, and not by RW.

Production began in 1938-39 of a pressure charger for diesel engines, driven by a turbine powered from the exhaust gases of the engine: it was for both land and marine use and the work was in the hands of T.B. Hall, C.J. Jackson and D.F. Hutchinson in the drawing office. This was a Brown-Boveri device (known as the Buchi type after its inventor). Charles Jackson recalls the first installation, on a Germn M.A.N. (all-welded) engine at Scott's yard on the Clyde. The Admiralty ordered three for "T" Class submarines — the first was fitted in HMS "Tribune". HMS "Thetis", tragically lost on trials just before the War, was of the same class, but not fitted with a Buchi pressure charger. Further orders came from J.G. Kincaid for fitting to their diesel engines for Merchant vessels, and some were installed in wooden-hulled minesweepers. At one stage of the War, says Charles Jackson, an order came for some 50 of these pressure chargers as part of 'digging machines' of some kind — it was believed locally that Churchill, with memories of trench warfare, had urged the ordering of these devices: the project was dropped, and the 50 blowers were never delivered, being scrapped after lying at the works for some time.

T.B. Hall was later to become Boiler Shop Manager — a post he held for many years.

The local Managing Director for most of the War years was Mr. Nithsdale, and he was succeeded in 1945 by Austen W. Walker, whose tenure lasted until 1950, when he left to join Air Products. Herbert S. Crace was Works Manager during the War, leaving at about the end of hostilities to acquire the local ship-repair business of F.O. Kindberg Ltd., which later serviced the "Mothball Fleet" of surplus naval craft laid up in Hartlepool Docks for some years. J.E. Smith, who had followed Herbert Crace as Works Manager, was Marine Director after the retirement of W.E. Loveridge. The Government quickly set up a programme for building merchant vessels, and Sir Summers Hunter, a director of the Richardsons Westgarth Group, was North-East Regional Director for that organisation. Hartlepool works was instructed to start on a series of sixteen re-heat Triple Expansion engines for tankers of 12,100 tons deadweight which were to be built at Furness Yard, Haverton Hill. These engines had cylinders of 27", 44" and 76" with a stroke of 51", rated at 3,650 IHP. Three boilers of 16'6" diameter were supplied, and all the associated pumps. Steam pressure was 220 psi. The first was Engine No. 2700 for "Empire Gold" (Furness Yard No. 325); her trials date was January 1941. The reheater had been designed originally by North Eastern Marine: the principle was to extract some heat from the steam before it entered the HP cylinder, and to use that heat to raise the temperature of the steam before it passed on to the IP and LP cylinders. The process kept the steam dry, and was said to show an economy of perhaps 10% over normal superheating. It went a long way to ensure that cylinder condensation (a very significant cause of thermal inefficiency in reciprocating engines) was more or less eliminated, as the steam exhausted from the LP cylinder still had some degree of superheat in it.

During 1941-42 the sister works of North Eastern Marine at Wallsend worked for a while on the design of a modified Burn diesel — one of five cylinders. Fred Taylor from Hartlepool worked at Wallsend for a time on that project, but it seems that nothing came of it.

Another item in the Merchant Ship construction programme was a series of cargo liners and tankers designed for a service speed of 15 knots. It was decided that these should be powered by geared turbine machinery of about 7,000 SHP, but the major turbine makers were heavily committed with vital orders for warships. As RW had the expertise to build the turbine sets required, as well as the necessary plant and equipment, the firm was appointed as principal supplier to the various shipyards which were to build these higher speed vessels. Before that series, however, two larger geared turbine sets were produced in 1943 for heavy-lift ships under construction at Vickers Yard, Barrow. These sets were of 8,000 SHP, driven by steam at 440 psig and 750 degrees F. from two RW-FW water-tube boilers. (Engine Nos. 2734-5).

In all these ships with turbine machinery from RW, which needed water-tube boilers, Foster Wheeler boilers were installed as standard from 1943 (from "Empire Viceroy", Engine No. 2734), and a whole series of thirty Ministry ships were fitted with turbine sets of 6,000 to 12,000 BHP. It was only in 1947 that locally built Doxfords once more appeared in the order book.

The works had orders for various other marine items, including the design in 1942 of a set of jigs for shell hoist detail for the "George V" class of battleships. Apprentices of the time recall the very fine quality 'pre-war' finish of some of this Admiralty work: war-time production was normally allowed a lower quality of finish than would have been permissible in peace-time.

There was a good deal of boiler work during the war for other shipyards, and boilers were regularly shipped by barge and tug to the Tees for Furness and Smith's Dock shipyards. On one occasion the barge sank and no trace of barge or boilers was ever found, in spite of expensive sweeps of the floor of Hartlepool Bay. From that time boilers despatched in this way had all openings closed off so that they would float.

The first land use boiler from Hartlepool works was built in 1944.

Developments of 1945 and Later

Hartlepool Works was called on to assist N.E.M. in 1945, when that section of the Group entered on its second diesel period with the production of the N.E.M.-Doxford — special tooks were sent up and a 1948 report, chronicling the despatch of the 100th N.E.M.-Doxford (NEM Contract 3334), said some of that equipment was still in use at N.E.M. North Eastern Marine had built Doxfords in the 1920's. The first post-World War II engine from the Tyne was for the "British Rose" in 1946 and within two years the production rate was over 40 working cylinders per annum.

In 1946 and 1947 Cunard ordered two set of turbine machinery for their "Asia" and "Arabia" from Laing's yard in Sunderland: obtaining this engine order against severe competition was a considerable achievement for Hartlepool, and the owners' satisfaction with those ships led to a repeat order for their "Assyria" in 1950 from the Swan, Hunter yard (Engine No. 2782).

In 1946 Foster-Wheeler devised an air-conditioning plant for marine use, and a set was made at the Hartlepool works for the tanker "British Empress", building at Furness Yard, Haverton Hill. Geoffrey Cox, an ex-apprentice from Richardsons, Westgarth (Hartlepool) served part of his sea time on the vessel, which was the first British merchant ship with air-conditioned accommodation: at least it was air-conditioned some of the time! The system was rather temperamental and that installation did not attract orders.

Then in 1948 the marine engine order book shows a series of six ships for Swedish owners, with Fiat-Ansaldo engines (2776-2881) built up and installed by Hartlepool works. After that date all the marine engines from the Hartlepool works were turbines, in power up to 17,500 BHP to a single screw for tankers of 40,000 tons deadweight built at Furness Yard, Haverton Hill.

In 1950 T.P. Everett became local Managing Director; he transferred to the nuclear side of the firm's activities in 1958. The Marine side of the Hartlepool operations was at this time in the hands of J.E. Smith.

One of the 1953 ships from Furness Yard (Yard No. 462 — Engine No. 2787) was the turbine vessel "Melika", fitted with semi-automatic engine room controls. At some stage in its commercial career the ship caught fire in the Gulf of Oman after collision with a French tanker, and was abandoned by the entire crew while still steaming along. After some time the Royal Navy were able to board the vessel by helicopter, still steaming, and stop the engines by means of the emergency vacuum breaker; they made complimentary remarks on the way the machinery had functioned for some time without human intervention! The ship was later repaired in Oman to an extent which allowed her to be towed to Bombay for a re-fit and full repairs: although the turbines had not been progressively cooled in the proper manner after the emergency stop, the shaft alignment of the turbines, when stripped down, was found to be perfect — yet another indication of the high quality of British Marine Engineers such as RW.

Engine room remote control systems were now leading the way to what became known as "unmanned machinery spaces" and RW created a separate company to concentrate on these pneumatic and electro-mechanical systems. That subsidiary was RW Instrumentation & Controls Ltd., later (from 1965) based on a Hartlepool Trading Estate, and H.O. ('Bert') Walker was the man responsible for the design concept of most of the wide range of control and data collection devices which the firm sold. The company soon obtained a sole licence from Drayton-Southern to manufacture and supply their data logging equipment. In 1979 its name was changed to Richwest Electronics.

The large power output of the sets ordered from Furness Yard, Haverton Hill, required very large propellers (about 23 feet in diameter), which were too large for road or rail transport. These manganese-bronze propellers were made at Charlton, shipped by Coast Lines vessels to Hartlepool, landed at Irvine's Quay and machined in Hartlepool works to fit the propeller shaft. The next problem was to deliver them to the stern of the ship (on the building ways) where there was only about five feet of water, and where two cranes — one of each side of the ways — could 'marry' to lift the weight of the large propeller. The writer, as shipbroker, chartered each time a local turtle-deck barge to carry the propeller from Hartlepool to Haverton Hill, where its shallow draught of water allowed the shipyard operations to take place. The lesson learned from the loss of a pair of boilers in Tees Bay a few years earlier meant that each propeller barged round to the Tees had attached to it a dan buoy on a long line and J.P. Sivewright, a local Marine Surveyor, was employed to check the lashings and the buoy attachment!

In April 1953 the Group stated the marine engine output from all its members for the period 1st August 1945 to 30th April 1953 "had been installed in 243 vessels whose total DWT was 1,728,977 tons, giving a total output of 835,520 HP. This is equivalent to supplying and installing machinery of 2980 HP every 7 working days throughout this period." In addition 210 "Boilers Only" contracts had been completed (108 multi-tubular type and 102 of the water-tube type).

In the Spring of 1958 a new Production Control Department, headed by W.G. Brown at Hartlepool, was set up to oversee the progress of the many items in the work-load through their various stages and co-ordinate production. (W.G. Brown's successor in that post — in 1960 — was T.E. Watson). In the summer of 1958 T.P. Everett, Managing Director at Hartlepool, left to become an Executive Director on atomic power station work, based in London, and was succeeded at Hartlepool by H. Watson-Jones. Tom Everett remained on the Group Board.

In the summer of 1960, not long after securing a licence to build Babcock & Wilcox type water-tube boilers, the first order came in — this was for two main boilers, each of 123,000 lbs/hour capacity and an auxiliary boiler of 20,000 lbs/hour for Shaw Savill's "Northern Star". Other orders followed, including two of 5,800 lbs/hour for B.P. Tankers (Contract D.562). At about this time W.G. Brown moved to be Turbine Shop Manager, and later Managing Director (Hartlepool).

The final full boilers & engine set from the Hartlepool works was for the steam turbine tanker "Gulf Finn" in April of 1961 (Engine No. 2810), one of a series for Gulf Oil. This vessel's two FW boilers produced steam at 600 psig (at the superheater outlet) and 850 degrees F. They had an evaporation capacity of 72,500 lbs per hour. That event more or less coincided with the surrender of the Brown-Boveri licence for turbine manufacture, after more than 60 years of co-operation between the two companies. This matter is further discussed in Chapter 30.

The boiler shops at Hartlepool were busy with a series of smaller FW boilers for whale-catchers built at Smith's Dock, South Bank: the vessels mostly came to Hartlepool for the installation of their new steam plant under the Fairbairn gooseneck crane at Irvine's Quay in the Old Harbour, convenient to the works.

23' DIAMETER PROPELLER.

W.E. Loveridge, in his paper which internal evidence suggests was probably written in 1957, gives a total of 234 marine water-tube boilers built up to that date: 112 for the company's own engines and 122 supplied to other engine builders. He says that no less than 76 repeat orders were secured for the comparatively small whale-catchers boilers, which had an evaporation rating of 17,000 lbs/hour. The Hartlepool work-force was in the region of 2500-3000 at that time, with about 300 apprentices (an annual intake of 60 for the five year period of service). By no means all of these employees were engaged on marine work, as the workload had a very large non-marine element.

The Group Board made a decision in 1956 that each of the operating companies should "be the beneficial owner of its property, plant, work-in-progress and stock-in-trade". After that had been implemented, with capital adjusted as necessary, the accounts showed the Hartlepool Works to have an authorised capital of £2 million, equal to half of the total capital of the Group, which was then employing 5636 people.

In 1956 the Group was extended by the purchase of Humber Graving Dock and Engineering Co. Ltd., founded in 1909 at the (then) new dock of Immingham, and in the following year was further enlarged when it took in Parsons Marine Steam Turbine Co. Ltd. of Wallsend—a descendant of the original turbine makers established by Sir Charles Parsons in 1894. This acquisition raised the total number of employees to 7566.

TYPICAL MARINE TURBINE ROTOR.

The Richardsons, Westgarth Group continued in its 1957 form until 1964, when George Clark and North Eastern Marine were combined into a new company (Geo. Clark & N.E.M. Ltd.) within the Group, but that combination did not originally include the Hartlepool Engine Works.

Lloyd's Class I welding approval, an increasingly necessary standard to have as the 1950's progressed, was obtained in 1958.

One difficult marine job obtained was the successful building of stainless steel boilers for a warship being built at Swan, Hunter's yard on the Tyne: this was a sub-contract from Babcock & Wilcox, and all the work was subject to rigorous examination by Admiralty inspectors.

The Board called in outside management consultants in the late 1950's (at considerable expense) to look at operations and put forward plans for rationalisation, new directions and new products. The Group Board had already decided (early in 1956) that diesel production at Hartlepool was to cease, though sub-contract work for N.E.M. on NEM-Doxford engines would continue for some time. It was said that there were enough turbine orders in hand and likely to be available in the future to allow concentration on land and marine turbines at Hartlepool — especially as customers were always wanting quick delivery of their orders, though at that time the marine market was causing some concern. Perhaps as a result of the consultants' advice the marine engine builders in the Group were put under the unified control of a new 'Marine Division', the better to co-ordinate their activities, and at the same time some non-marine work was introduced into three of these operating companies, including Hartlepool Engine Works.

British shipbuilding was seriously in decline, the number of ships being built world-wide was shrinking, and the low-speed diesel of very large size — the 'cathedral' engine — was much in vogue for the larger and ever larger tankers and bulk carriers being built. Some of these vessels had turbine machinery, which demanded extremely large water-tube boilers — such units were beyond the capacity of the Hartlepool Works. Even if they could have been built on the 'island' site at Middleton it would have been impossible to move them out by land, and shipment of them would have needed heavy expenditure on Irvine's Quay and/or more heavy cranage there or at the North Basin. Before many years were to pass number of large second and third generation container ships were to have their turbine propelling machinery removed and be fitted with low-speed diesel engines (giving a lower service speed) in an effort to reduce fuel costs. Most of that work went to the Far East. The demand for marine engines from British makers had shrunk to an all-time low, and from 1961 Richardsons Westgarth at Hartlepool made no more marine propulsion plants. During the sixty-one years from its incorporation into the Group, Hartlepool Engine Works had supplied engines for more than 500 ships — and, in the case of the steamers, the boilers, pumps, condensers and other ancillaries. Operations had covered the three major types of propelling machinery; steam reciprocating, steam turbine and diesel. (By 1964 the position had so deteriorated that it was considered necessary to close down the Parsons Marine Steam Turbine Company plant on the Tyne.)

Looking through the stator casing of Richborough No. 2 set, which frames the engine and gearing for the "Gulf Briton", erected for shop testing. In the background can be seen part of the Engineering Division's de-aerator test rig.

Non-Marine Work

The main intention of this review has been to concentrate on the marine side of Richardsons Westgarth's work at Hartlepool, but the non-marine work must be mentioned, though it deserves more study than is given to it in this paper. A major part of their order books in many years consisted of the production of land plant, and in particular electrical generating equipment.

The supply of non-marine equipment was already a significant feature of the works output when the amalgamation of 1900 took place, and the manufacture of reciprocating machinery for electrical generation (for industrial use) had been carried on from 1897, under an agreement with the Swiss firm of Brown-Boveri. The early production would be based on direct current.

In 1903, as the Brown-Boveri agreement had been extended to turbines, a new shop was erected at Hartlepool for their production. Five sets for driving generators were made in the first year, and the largest (of 750 kW) was for Cargo Fleet Iron, which was a Furness-controlled company.

Turbine sizes soon increased: in 1904 to 1,500 kW, in 1907 to 5,600 kW and rising by 1917 to 25,000 kW. Over 120 turbine sets were delivered for land use in the years 1903-17, together with their associated condensers and pumps. Turbine production continued after World War I.

About 1922, when RW were first supplying the turbines for a Portobello power station, one Ulrich Signer, a Swiss turbine engineer, came from Brown-Boveri to supervise the installation and commissioning of the plant. After that was complete, perhaps two years later, he moved to Hartlepool, where he stayed at RW on the turbine side, dealing with both marine and non-marine work. Later one of his sons (also Ulrich) joined him at Hartlepool Engine Works, and was an apprentice in 1938.

Before 1928 RW had supplied only the prime movers for various applications including the generation of alternating current electricity, but the Directors took the decision in that year to extend the operations to building alternators. Proven designs were available from their Swiss partners, and so a new shop was built on the Middleton site. The decision may well have been influenced by the fact that the standard alternating current frequency in Britain was being changed from 40 Herz to 50 Herz, creating a demand for new plant. This extension of activities meant, of course, that RW and Contraflo could now offer boilers, condensers, pumps, de-aerators, other ancillaries, turbines and now alternators — all the major components of a power station.

In 1936 the first RW-BB 30,000 kW set was supplied — this was for Portobello Power Station, a station which had been using a Hartlepool turbine for 14 years. By then turbine speed was 3,000 rpm; the earlier standard speed had been 1500 rpm.

Some orders after that date were still for turbines only, to drive competitors' alternators, but RW soon secured alternator business in growing sizes, and in 1939 supplied a 30,000 kW set to Stockport, whither it had been diverted from its original destination of Willesden, due to wartime needs.

During the Second World War (in 1942) an axial flow blower of Brown-Boveri design, built originally for a Velox boiler, was converted to power the only large wind-tunnel available in Britain for Government aeronautical research.

Work in 1939-45 included a 30,000 kW turbo-alternator set for Willesden Power Station, with an alternator producing 22,000 volts — a far higher voltage than had then been made at Hartlepool. There was a good deal of worry at the design stage and when the high voltage testing started, but the set was a success.

Towards the end of the War a small number of portable power-packs were built, with an output of about 2,500 kW. These consisted of a 'compact' Foster-Wheeler boiler, complete with oil firing gear, pumps and so on, plus turbine and alternator with switchgear: their purpose was to provide a ready-made electrical supply to areas devastated by war.

Boiler sizes for land use could be very substantial — a boiler set supplied to the Fleetwood Power Station had an evaporation capacity of 300,000 lbs per hour. This set had a new system for blowing the pulverised fuel into the furnaces, and until effective sealing of the fan unit had been achieved deposits of fine coal dust went everywhere. Up to 1957 RW's boiler with the highest operating pressure was one of 1,000 psig, built for the Pametrada Turbine Research Station, on the Tyne.

Brown-Boveri had experimented with gas turbines as early as 1908, but were defeated by the lack of suitable materials for the high temperatures involved. By 1939 they had achieved success with continental power generating installations.

RW took up a Brown-Boveri licence on gas turbines in 1954 and very soon obtained their first order (from Shelton Iron & Steel of Staffordshire): this was the first such set ever built for use in a British steelworks, to run on blast-furnace gas, gas and gas-oil or gas-oil alone, with an output of 2,500 kW. The Hartlepool works was greatly assisted in this proejct by Peter Heer, who came from Brown-Boveri for the project, and was described as "a tower of strength". After the plant had completed all its local tests, it was allowed to remain at Hartlepool for some time, so that it could be demonstrated on four separate days to potential customers, including the Admiralty, and to the technical press. Charles Jackson and H.O. Walker showed the plant running at full load. After installation at Shelton and the agreed maintenance period the set was taken over by the client on 14th April 1959 (C.5778).

Further orders for similar but larger plants followed — one for two units from Kuwait and another for two units from the Pakistan Industrial Development Corporation.

One unusual 1957 task was the reconditioning of a German built Blast-furnace Turbo-blower for Stewarts & Lloyds at Corby: this machine had been part of German reparations, not used earlier. Turbine business was increasing at this time, and a start was made on preparations for a new Turbine Shop on the Middleton site, on the south side of the road which ran through the works.

According to the Autumn 1958 issue of "The Link" work in hand at Hartlepool at that time included: —

The commissioning of the last of a series of six 60 MW turbo-alternator sets for Brighton 'B' Power Station (C.5771).

The last of the three 100,000 lbs/hr W.T. boilers for Cargo Fleet (F.128)

Two 'Economic' boilers of 15,000 lbs/hr for Smith & Butler of Leeds (E.206) and one of 10,000 lbs/hr for Commercial Plastics.

An extraction condensing turbo-generator set for export to Saskatchewan (C.5803)

Gas turbine generating unit for Shelton Iron & Steel, Staffs. (C.5778)

Three 125,000 lbs/hr W.T. boilers for South Durham Iron & Steel of West Hartlepool (F.131); one 80,000 lbs/hr W.T. boiler for Courtaulds at Preston (F.132); a second 3,125 kW pass-out condensing steam turbine for Thames Board, Purfleet (C.5790); condensing and feed heating plant of the 60 MW No. 3 turbo-alternator set at South Denes Power Station (C.5785); and the first 3,000,000 gallons/hr Rotary Water Strainer for C.E.G.B. at Belvedere (C.5777)

and much other work besides, including the following contracts: — C.5792, T.A.5230, C.5785, C.5798 — for Pakistan, C.5800 & 5804, C.5812 & 5813, C.5805, C.5807 & 5808, F.134 and C.5809 — for Kuwait.

After the end of marine engine and boiler work the Company continued to build land-based generating machinery, supplying the boilers and much of the associated plant as well as the rotating machinery.

Another useful line of production at Hartlepool was "Deptford" rotary water strainers (mentioned above) for all kinds of circulating water systems, and up to 1957 some 67 had been made. They varied in capacity from 100,000 gallons per hour to 5 million gallons per hour. The New Zealand Government installed these strainers in their geothermal power station at Wairakei (C.5793 and C.5814), and a number of other export orders were obtained.

The post-war 60 MW cross-compound sets of RW-BB turbo-alternators for Portobello Power Station, Edinburgh, were judged to be the most efficient installation in the country, and held that record for at least four years. The initial set of this type (C.5686 — ordered in 1948, delivered in 1952) was RW's first 60 MW turbo-alternator set, and the whole process from tendering to final installation and commissioning was the particular responsibility of local director Bernard Wyatt. B.B.Wyatt was a very tall man of some eccentricity, enormous charm and enthusiasm, well-known in a number of circles both locally and nationally. A 'larger than life' character of considerable mathematical ability, he claimed that the cost of his annual holiday on the French Riviera was always recouped in the casino by use of a mathematical system of his own devising — and this before the day of the computer.

Other non-marine output over the years was in the form of turbo-blowers for blast furnaces, turbo gas exhausters (of which 36 were made) and ten high pressure/back pressure sets for Imperial Chemical Industries. The first order for boilers for industrial applications had been obtained in 1944, and in the next 13 years 55 boilers were supplied for various industrial applications. Reciprocating pumping engines for water works had been produced by Thomas Richardsons long before 1900 and there were further orders for such plant in 1904 (Antwerp — Nos. 1173-75), 1905 (South Hampshire — No. 1196) and 1906 a triple for Staffordshire Potteries (No. 1209); for some reason all these sets are listed on the marine engines order book; perhaps because they were triple expansion engines.

Extended and improved facilities for the manufacture of larger Turbo-Alternator sets at Hartlepool South Works were completed in 1959.

Early in 1960 an advertisement appeared in a Pakistan newspaper offering for sale from a textile mill two RW turbine generating sets of 100 kW output (200 amperes at 500 volts D.C.). These had been made in 1931 (Contract No. C.5491) for an Indian Rajah's palace power supply and the Company was pleased to note that they were still in working order and ready for further use after nearly thirty years, though Hartlepool had no knowledge of when the plant was transferred from the palace to the textile mill.

LINK, SPRING 1960.

ELECTRIC MACHINERY
FOR SALE

RICHARDSON WESTGARTH, BROWN BOVERI, STEAM TURBINES MANUFACTURED BY RICHARDSON WESTGARTH & CO., LTD., HARTEPOOL. 2 SETS, WITH D. D. C. DYNAMOS OPEN COMPOUND BOUND TYPE, 100 KW EACH, 500 VOLTS, 200 AMPERES, 3,000 REVOLUTIONS, CONTINUOUS RATING. EACH WITH JET CONDENSING AND PUMPING SETS COMPLETE WITH ELECTRIC MOTORS WITH SWITCH-STARTERS OFFERED FOR READY SALE. FOR FURTHER PARTICULARS PLEASE WRITE TO RAHMANIA TEXTILE MILLS, LTD., JHANG ROAD, LYALLPUR.

TURBINE.

"The Link" issue of Autumn 1960 reported the official inspection of a back-pressure 9,500 kW "extra high pressure" turbo-alternator set for Margam Steelworks at Port Talbot: this was to operate at 3000 psig and 1050 degrees F. and was claimed to be the highest temperature and pressure in the country for any such plant. (C.5805). As this item was "a completely new design of pioneering character" — to quote 'The Link' of Summer 1959 — it was considered that its successful commissioning would be of great importance to the Company.

Later that year RW had installed a new balancing and overspeed plant for rotating machinery. It was capable of dealing with pieces up to 65 tons weight at speeds up to 4,500 rpm, and was driven by a home built steam turbine of 8,000 HP.

Weir-Westgarth Ltd. was formed in 1963 to make 'Flash' Evaporators. This was a joint venture with G. & J. Weir of Glasgow in the manufacture of this type of Evaporator, originally for producing fresh water for boiler feed from salt water by use of a partial vacuum to evaporate the sea-water at a lower temperature than under atmospheric pressure. The principle was applied to de-salination plants and a number were sold — all for export to countries in and around the Persian Gulf, to Gibraltar, Chile and other destinations.

W.G. Brown was promoted in 1963 from Turbine Shop Manager to local Managing Director at Hartlepool, remaining in that post for some 5 years before he left for new pastures. His final successor, after brief reigns by J.D. Glanville, J.T. Boddington and B. Crowdy, was J. Campbell Murray, who was soon to spend part of his working week at Wallsend.

The Company's proven excellence in welding enabled it to secure work as a sub-contractor to John Laing's Anglo-French consortium on node manufacture for the large oil jackets "Graythorp I" and "Graythorp II", built on William Gray's old Graythorp-on-Tees site for the Forties Field in the North Sea.

Prior to North Sea natural gas being brought ashore, when traditional coal-gas plants were being phased out, Hartlepool works built a number of gas-making plants for the Gas Board: these were ICI designed plants, using a feedstock of naphtha: the rather lean gas thus produced was enriched with butane. Notable examples of such plants were those for Hartlepool and Killingholme.

When Monsanto set up their chemical plant on Seal Sands in the 1960's RW (Hartlepool) secured the order for all the pipe-work on this Badger-designed installation of considerable complexity. D.F. Hutchinson was in charge of that contract.

A general view of the new balancing and over-speed test pit at Hartlepool. The drive turbine is located behind the wall at the back of the photograph.

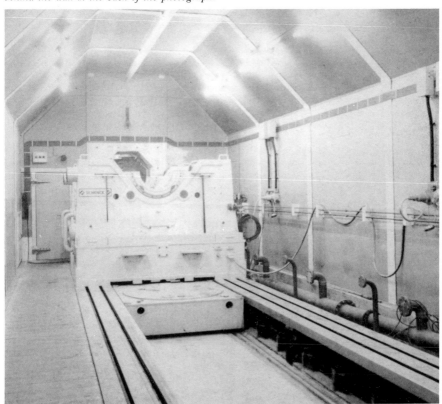

Two aerial views of the Hartlepool Works of Richardsons Westgarth in the 1950's.

The Beginning of the End for Hartlepool

In 1961 the Brown-Boveri licence was given up by mutual consent — the reasons are not entirely clear, and some sources say it was much regretted by the Swiss patentees. One reason quoted to the author for this severing of the old relationship was that RW wanted to develop designs of their own in fields where Brown-Boveri were active, and the Swiss would not allow this under the agreement. Other sources suggest the more cogent reason that the principal non-marine customer, the C.E.G.B., wanted other turbine types than Brown-Boveri in their later power stations, and that those be of U.K. design and manufacture. In addition the increasing size of turbo-alternator sets required a single-shaft in-line design, which was in total conflict with the Brown-Boveri cross-compound multi-shaft philosophy. One consequence of this was a notable increase in the design work which had to be done in Hartlepool, and the establishment of what proved to be an ineffective work-sharing agreement with General Electric. G.E.C. turbines were then built at Hartlepool, but not for very long, and eventually the Board decided to cease production of rotating machinery: that took place in December 1967, and the South Works at Hartlepool was closed, though parts were later leased to other business undertakings. The concentration was then on fabrication and general engineering in the North Works.

The Central Electricity Generating Board, successor to the Central/British Electricity Authority, which had (on the nationalisation of the electricity industry) assumed the responsibility for all power generating in Britain, was continually increasing the size of generating units ordered, rising through 350 MW to 500 MW and even 650 MW per turbo-alternator unit: there was never a standard size and design for long, whether for conventional or nuclear stations. Larger generating sets meant larger boilers, perhaps up to an evaporation capacity of 1 million pounds per hour, and the turbines and alternators were becoming extremely large. These bigger units showed some economy in the unit cost of power generated, and the steady growth in generator size seemed a long-term trend. Making the larger pieces would demand very substantial re-equipment of the works, and in any case there were problems in getting ever greater weights off the site by land, since it was virtually an island. One informant suggests that any generating plant with units above 120 MW would consist of units too large to be manufactured and handled in the shops as they then existed, and too heavy for road transport off the Middleton site, in view of the weight restrictions on the swing-bridge in Middleton Road, although a new approach road through the docks had been made in 1959. By that year Hartlepool was busy on the manufacture of a 120 MW unit for Richborough Power Station (C.5812), and overhead cranes of 100 tons and 175 tons had been commissioned in the Mid Bay and the Turbine Shop extensions, together with additional machine tools.

Estimating for Power Station tenders had become an increasing financial burden. At one point this meant Richardsons Westgarth (Hartlepool) having, the writer believes, no less than three separate design teams working on tenders for the CEGB — as had other competitors in the field. The cost of prepararing a tender of these "mega" power stations was enormous, and if no order were obtained that expenditure was in no way recoverable. Costs of this nature were a heavy burden, and may well have been a significant factor in the rationale for ending the manufacture of all major rotating machinery at the Hartlepool works, especially after disappointments like that over the Wylfa Power Station in Anglesey: the Company's sanguine expectation of a very major contract for that work was dashed, though some components were supplied, the larger and heavier items being delivered by sea from Hartlepool to Holyhead.

The company's last contract with the CEGB was for the condensing and feed-heating plants for an oil-fired Power Station at Pembroke — the official opening of that station was by Edward Heath.

Attempts were made to find other products to fill at least part of the works, and one line was the 'Maxecon' boiler package, for industrial installations, hospitals and other large institutions. This source of relatively low pressure steam was patented by RW in the name of J.S. Laundon, and it was he who nursed it into production from 1956. In spite of the equipment receiving a good press, the flow of orders fell eventually to a level that was not adequate to support the boiler shops as an economic operation. These 'packaged' boilers, designed for economy, were built in sizes with evaporation rates from 5,000 to 60,000 lbs/hr at pressures of 100 to 300 psig and temperature of 600 degrees (F). T.P. Macklam, who was for some time in charge of the 'Maxecon' project, achieved a level of orders of about 50 units per annum for what was undoubtedly a good product, but later the sales fell off — perhaps his successors were not able to put into their task the same level of technical expertise which promoted sales. For the year 1965/6 a sales target of 50 units had been set, and for the year 1966/67 the target was 120 units: sales continued to disappoint, but even so some 650 units were sold during the eighteen year period 1956-1984.

In 1961 Gordon Hunter (the third generation of his family in the business) became Managing Director of the Group, and made 1964 a year of considerable changes, including steps to co-ordinate the activities of the North East companies. RW (Instrumentation & Controls) was created to take over work in that field already in hand at Hartlepool Engine Works, RW (Transmissions) was formed by the friendly take-over of the gear division of George Angus & Co., Hebburn, and RW (Engineering) was set up to take over the non-marine side of installation and maintenance. The latter company was based at Stokesley, under the control of Tony Folland from Hartlepool Works. At much the same time George Clark of Sunderland and North Eastern Marine of Wallsend were welded into one company (George Clark & N.E.M. Ltd.). The closure of the Turbinia Works (Parsons Marine) completed this series of changes, and 45 items of plant from that operation were bought by Hartlepool works for £5,700.

The Board of RW (Hartlepool) now comprised Gordon L. Hunter (Chair), W. G. Brown (M.D.), C. J. Jackson (Commercial Director), J. C. Murray (Technical Director) and G. R. Robinson, Secretary. One of the recurring items before the Directors was the production delays caused by a shortage of skilled labour and of draughtsmen: as one writes in 1994 it seems strange that this was so, and that newspaper advertisements in various parts of the country produced little or no result.

O. J. Philipson, whose term as Vice-Chairman or Chairman of the Group had covered 38 years, retired from the Group chair in 1965, being succeeded by A. D. McN.Boyd. A policy of diversification was set, and an 80% stake in Haigh & Ringrose (electrical contractors) was acquired. The annual report for 1965 shows the disappointment with the modest volume of work coming from the arrangement to work with GEC on turbines and other plant for generation stations: the outcome of this 'agreement' with GEC was never anything other than extremely disappointing. One instance of this was the offer to Hartlepool by GEC of supplying some units of the plant for Didcot Power at prices that were described as "extremely low" and could only result in the works making a substantial loss on their manufacture.

S. W. McColl, Hartlepool Production Controller, joined the Board in June 1966 as Works Director.

In December of 1967 the South Works (rotating machinery) was closed rather later than had been planned, andall work transferred across the road to the North Works at Hartlepool, where additional machinery had been installed: the workforce was then reduced to some 1,200. The Weir-Westgarth evaporator business was proving increasingly unprofitable, and the RW stake was sold to Weirs. W. G. Brown resigned as a director, and J. T. Boddington was appointed Hartlepool Managing Director. By this time Foster-Wheeler had set up a manufacturing facility in Hartlepool, had been recruiting from the Hartlepool Works people, and were now suggesting that they might well start making marine boilers in their Brenda Road factory.

The Hartlepool Managing Director J. T. Boddington resigned on 29th May 1969, and was replaced by J. D. Glanville, who in his turned resigned in 1972.

In 1970 the Richardsons, Westgarth name disappeared from Middleton, as Hartlepool Engine Works became part of the George Clark-N.E.M. operation within the Group: the Hartlepool North Works was sold to GC-NEM for the sum of £2,071,892: the South Works, now closed, remained with the Company. This change was followed by the installation of more new plant at Middleton, and the works was much involved in machining and fitting work for the engine-building programmes of the other members of the Group. At the same time a new facility for the production of spare parts was set up at Hartlepool works. After 1st April 1970 all RW (Hartlepool) Board meetings took place in the Group offices at

Wallsend, and were concerned with secretarial and financial matters from that point onwards: in effect RW (Hartlepool) had ceased to be an operating company within the Richardsons, Westgarth Group and in 1976 the Registered Office of RW (Hartlepool) was moved to Wallsend (c/o Richardsons, Westgarth & Co. Ltd.).

The Group diversification strategy led to the 1972 acquisition of C. & C. Wright of Grimsby, steel stockholders, and their operations were merged with the steel stockholding side of Humber Graving Dock to create Humber Steel Stockholders, still part of the Group in 1994. For many years past most of the companies in the RW Group had been involved, albeit on a small scale, in steel stockholding operations, so this activity was not a new concept. During that year the Group Board was forced to expend a great deal of time (and money) on fighting off an unwelcome take-over bid from Leeds Assets — a company used as a vehicle by Jessel Securities, one of the acquisitive young financial companies of the day. In the end the RW shareholders supported the Directors' advice and rejected the Leeds Assets offer. J. D. Glanville resigned from the Hartlepool Board in August of 1972 and was replaced as a Director by D. W. Spencer. The disused South Works was let on a 3-year lease to British Nuclear Design at a rental of £40,000 per annum, and the following year the Company surrendered to the Hartlepool Port Authority the 1953 lease of some land on the dock estate.

The Group continued with friendly acquisitions, and in 1973 added Eric C. Flower of Sheffield, contract plumbers and heating engineers, also S. P. Gears & Instrumentations of Sidcup. This activity was followed in 1974-5 by the addition of a number of new elements: —

> E. Gerald Ltd., steel stockholders, decoilers and processors of Manchester; Hemisphere Metal of Shoeburyness in Essex, stockholders; Simpsons of Spalding (makers of commercial glasshouses), P. Buyers of Aberdeen (ship & offshore suppliers), 75% of Cromarty Firth Engineers (largely involved in North Sea work), and the formation of two new companies — R & G Steels, intended to trade internationally in metals and RW Offshore, to extend operations from Aberdeen, as this was now the centre of activity for the North Sea oilfields.

New gearboxes for Tower Bridge were supplied by RW (Transmissions), with attendant press publicity.

Tunstall Court, until 1925 the home of Lord Furness in West Hartlepool, had been given to Hartlepool Works for use as a sports and social club. In 1973, after board-room and legal discussion of the matter from 1969, also consultation with Furness interests, the land and house were sold by RW (Hartlepool) to the local authority for the sum of £35,000. Boardroom changes continued: in May of 1975 the Minutes of Hartlepool Board meetings record the resignations of D. W. Spencer and of John Campbell Murray, and the appointment of A. D. McN.Boyd and Raymond Bates. D. F. R. Foord took over from P. Tarbitt as Company Secretary.

The Group took a 75% stake in a new Scottish company formed in 1975, called Preventive & Predictive Maintenance (Scotland) Ltd., which was aimed mainly at the offshore oil industry. This was the year in which the Government began to flesh out its proposals for the nationalisation of the whole of the British shipbuilding industry, and it was clear that a substantial part of the RW Group would fall within the net; this prospect no doubt prompted further ventures into offshore work and steel stockholding in the acquiring of J. M. Mouat (Shetland based) and of Highland Steels & Supplies Ltd. By the end of 1975 the accounts showed that almost one quarter of the Group's turnover came from stockholding and merchanting operations.

In 1976 the Group Board deployed every possible argument against the inclusion in the then Labour Government's nationalisation plans of Hartlepool Works (now very largely non-marine) and of the Humber Graving Dock & Engineering Co., but to no avail as far as the former works was concerned, and on Vesting Day (1st July 1977) the works at Wallsend, Sunderland and Hartlepool became part of British Shipbuilders — Humber G.D. & E. was not taken. The RW Board pointed out that the three operations taken had been "set fair for a full year's profit of about £1 million" for 1977, and virtually all of that was lost to the Group. The effect of the nationalisation was to remove 100% of what the Group had been from 1938 to 1956, together with one quarter of the turnover and much more than one quarter of the employees. The wisdom and value of the diversification policy was now apparent.

It was at this point that the Hartlepool Works became part of the Clark-Hawthorn division of British Shipbuilders, and after three years of struggle the final blow came in 1981, when the Hartlepool works closed down: the attempts to find new products and new markets had not been successful enough, unfortunately, and it was a very sad day for the workforce and indeed for the town when work ceased on the Middleton site.

The last Managing Director at Hartlepool (under British Shipbuilders) was John Campbell Murray, who divided his time between Wallsend and Hartlepool, and Don Hutchinson was the last Works Manager on the Hartlepool site; it fell to him and his Assistant, Brian Threadkell, to lock the gates for the last time. The latter had earlier been a Foreman in the Heavy Machine Shop at RW (Hartlepool).

In one way the Richardsons Westgarth name lives on locally in land and marine engineering. A Teesside firm, appreciating that there was potential business in being able to offer spares for the many items of plant built at Hartlepool, some of which were long-lived, made an offer for the drawings: Bob Dickens and his colleagues at Bringover Ltd. (of Thornaby) purchased about ten tons of drawing and data, so that they could tender for work overhauling RW-made plant and manufacturing spares to order. In addition to the drawings some specialist machine tools were acquired from RW; Brian Threadkell, Works Manager (who is a former RW apprentice on the turbine side, and was the last Assistant Works Manager at RW Hartlepool), feels very much at home in Bringover's machine shop. That operation is still continuing in 1994 as this history is being compiled.

RW in the Nuclear Field

Richardsons Westgarth Atomic Ltd. was set up early in the post-war years, and this led to the Group's involvement, with others, in an associated Company in that field. Several consortia were set up in the immediate post-war period to undertake the very large civil and mechanical engineering works required by atomic power stations, and among these the fifth was "Atomic Power Constructions Ltd.", which consisted of several partners — Richardsons Westgarth, Crompton Parkinson, International Combustion of Derby and Fairey Engineering, who together were responsible for the generating plant. The civil works were carried out by Nuclear Civil Constructors Ltd. itself a partnership between Trollope & Colls and Holland, Hannen & Cubitts. Harry Fothergill was to be Chairman of the new consortium. Much of RW's work in this field (and in other new fields) was based on the design activities of the Group Engineering Division led by Dr. Frankel.

The head office was established in London, near to the corridors of power, and George Raby, who had been the Turbine Shop Manager at Hartlepool from 1928 to 1934, was appointed in 1957 to be Managing Director. He was joined there by Tom Everett, transferred from his position as M.D. of Hartlepool works.

Trawsfynydd Nuclear Power Station in North Wales was the first major contract for this consortium — an unusual station which included a high-level lake into which water was pumped in off-peak periods: during peak demand times the water could be released through turbines to give additional generating output. The site was landscaped by Sir Basil Spence, who had made his reputation with Coventry Cathedral. The large and heavy items which had to be shipped from Hartlepool were discharged at the tiny almost obsolete harbour of Portmadoc. As Portmadoc was only accessible on Spring tides the shipments needed accurate timing, and this constraint gave some problems to the company and to the author, who was employed as RW's chartering broker for these and numerous other movements in the post-war years. Former employees of RW tend to describe Trawsfynydd as "magic" — explaining that 'everywhere you look you see the RW label on the machinery in that power station'. The Group's house magazine "The Link" of Summer 1959 reported the award of the Trawsfynydd contract for the whole of the generating plant for this 500 MW station. The main contract comprised the RW-Brown-Boveri steam turbo-alternators with condensing and feed-heating systems, and that part of the contract was for the Hartlepool Works — the largest single order they had ever secured. The blowers for the carbon dioxide gas used to cool the reactors, plus associated pipework and equipment were also to be supplied by the Group. Wallsend had done the preliminary design and research work on the gas system but the work was eventually spread round Group factories, as was much other general engineering work for Trawsfynydd.

The A.P.C. consortium secured a substantial amount of installation work in connection with the Dungeness Nuclear Station and built part of the plant at Wylfa Station in Anglesey. There had been hopes of a very much larger order for the Wylfa project.

In mid-1960 the RW Group announced that Atomic Power Constructions Ltd. and the GEC/Simon-Carves atomic group had set up a jointly-owned company named United Power Co. Ltd. The new organisation would take over responsibility for future tenders for nuclear and other power stations, and would be based in the London offices of Atomic Power Constructions Ltd. The outcome of that venture was very disappointing, and it never yielded anything like the workload that had been anticipated; eventually, in 1968, the RW Group withdrew from any direct participation in the atomic power station field.

The Subsequent History of the Group

The nationalisation of three major units in 1977 resulted in a total compensation payment of £3.7 million, made up of several elements, paid to the RW Group in the form of Government Stocks, and the greatly altered Group continued on its adopted new course, extending its stockholding operations to Hull in 1977 through the take-over of Gardiner, Barugh & Jones.

In July 1978, on the resignation of Gordon Hunter and A. D. McN.Boyd, the chair of the RW (Hartlepool) Board was taken by G. E. Darwin, with Raymond Bates and D. F. R. Foord as colleagues: the latter had previously been Company Secretary and was succeeded in that post by A. R. Arrowsmith. Later, from 1980 to 1982 the Secretary's position was occupied by Kevin J. Middis. The main activity of the RW (Hartlepool) board seems to have consisted in these later years largely of holding an Annual General Meeting each year, as the Company was by then no longer an operating unit within the RW Group.

In 1980 a specialist air compressor firm (Airman Industrial Products) joined the Group.

The Humber Graving Dock & Engineering Co. had escaped the nationalisation net of 1977, and in 1981 tendered for the construction of an advanced and sophisticated diving support vessel ("Orelia") for Houlder Offshore, which was part of the Furness-Withy Group. This was a state-of-the-art project, and as is so often the case with high technology projects, it ran into trouble. Modifications to the design during construction pushed up the price by over £2 million to about £20 million, but even so it became apparent by late 1982 or early 1983 that the builders would make a substantial loss on the contract. The extent of that loss reached such proportions that it gave the Group serious financial problems: as a consequence, in February 1984 the fixed assets of Humber were sold, and work reduced merely to the completion of the "Orelia". She was delivered to her owners in June of 1984, with considerable relief, and the Humber Graving Dock operations then ceased.

Haigh & Ringrose and the Burgess business were sold in March 1984, and RW Transmissions was disposed of in the August.

By 1985 the reorganisation of the Group was largely complete, with its principal business restricted to stockholding and merchanting—and so it continues successfully to this day at various locations, with the Head Office at Kidderminster. In 1992 the Richardsons Westgarth Group employees numbered about 300: a very different picture indeed from the heyday of the organisation when it had over 7,500 people on the payroll and was a leading name in marine and land engineering. It is an ironic twist that the combination formed in 1900 by the drive and acumen of Sir Christopher Furness, founder of Furness, Withy & Co., had been brought near to callapse eightyfour years later as the result of a disastrous loss on an unfortunate contract with Houlder Offshore, a constituent part of the Furness-Withy organisation.

Apprenticeship & Training

The former apprentices whom the author has asked for their views and experiences are mostly in agreement that their time at RW was usefully spent, and valuable training during which they gained a wide range of engineering experience. In later life one of them (Lawrence Walker) was to have under him (at sea in a B.P. tanker) a junior engineer whose training had fairly obviously not been too good, and who expressed to his superior his regret at not having received the first-rate training which was given where his own father had served his time—"at a little place on the North East Coast" he said; "I think it was called Richardsons".

The training given seems to have been in advance of that in some works, and also the responsibility given to apprentices. One (Geoffrey Cox) recalls that as an apprentice he was sent to Furness Shipyard with others to level up the bedplates for the engines—he found, when he worked at another yard, that such a task was journeyman's work, and that no apprentices would be allowed to undertake it.

The Company was a participant in the North-East Coast Apprentice Advancement Scheme, under which marks were given for time-keeping, progress at work and class performance; monetary awards were given, depending on marks obtained, and not less than half of any award had to be spent on books, tuition fees or instruments. Each year a printed booklet was issued, with full details of marks achieved and awards earned. The D. B. Morison Scholarship, competed for annually, earned the holder a year at King's College, Newcastle. Robert Bull, who was apprentice from 1923 to 1928, still has (in 1994) his text-books from that time — obtained under the Advancement Scheme. His hours were 7.30 a.m. to noon and 1 p.m. to 5 p.m. from Monday to Friday and on Saturdays 7.30 a.m. to noon. From September to May each year he spent three evenings each week at night school and was given two evenings homework. He recalls that the first year's fee for evening classes for the 14-15 year old boys (working as boy labourers while waiting for an apprenticeship at 16) was 5 shillings — equal to one week's wages. In addition to the September-May evening classes for apprentices there were voluntary summer courses at the Technical College in Lauder Street, West Hartlepool — one on Naval Architecture which Robert Bull joined was in those days taken by Mr. Nixon, who was Foreman of the Moulding Loft at Irvine's shipyard in the West Harbour.

The 1938 and 1939 lists (retained by Don Hutchinson) show more than 250 apprentices, spread over fourteen departments: the greater concentrations of numbers were: — 80 in the Fitting & Erection Shops, 26 in the Machine Shops, 32 in the Boiler Shop, 57 in the Turbine Shop and 18 in the Iron Foundry. The 1939 list even shows one apprentice on the sheer-legs at the North Basin.

Some of the apprentices were trained as "Fitter & Turner", and not just one or the other — the author is led to believe that was not always common practice in marine engineering, though it certainly occurred across the Basin at Central Marine. One at least (Bill Shout) joined the Navy in war-time after a little over three years of his apprenticeship, and came back in 1947 to RW, where it was readily agreed to consider that his sea time as an Engine-room Artificer could be taken into the reckoning of his training and experience, and he was granted a completion certificate accordingly. He was the son of a skilled (time-served) machinist at RW — perhaps this had something to do with the way he was treated.

There were many 'characters' in the workforce, and some of them keep recurring in the reminiscences of former apprentices, such as Robert Chambers, Boiler Shop Foreman, who was unable to pass a boiler in the shop without giving it a ringing blow with a large hammer — a habit which earned him the nickname of "Rattler Bob". Many a young man who was taking it easy in a boiler under construction emerged from his hiding place holding his head as a result of the foreman's hammer-blows. Certainly the general view is that the foremen and charge-hands were men of real engineering skill and ability, as were many of the men (and girls in the alternator shop) who worked under them.

K. B. Eddison joined RW (Hartlepool) in 1956 on leaving the Regular Army and was in charge of apprentices, in addition to his other personnel duties: his recollection is that there would be about 280-300 apprentices at that time, and a total workforce of about 2500 at Hartlepool. "The Link" of 1958 reports the setting-up of a new Apprentice School in Hartlepool works, attended on a full-time basis by apprentices just starting their engineering training.

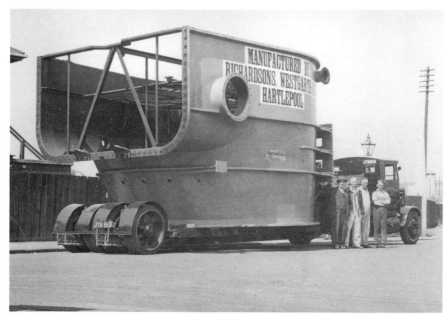

Condenser for Portobello Power Station loaded up ready for transport. Contract C.380 June 1949.

Shaping Boiler Plate.

Sources

Printed Material:

Major R. Martin:
"Historical Notes on West Hartlepool and its Founder" (R. Martin, West Hartlepool 1925).

Sir Cuthbert Sharp: "A History of Hartlepool" (Hartlepool Borough Council 1978 Edition).

B. G. Spalding: "Shipbuilders of The Hartlepools" (Hartlepool Borough Council 1986).

Lloyd's Register of Ships.

Index of British patents.

MacGibbon et al: "B.O.T. & Marine Engineering Knowledge" (Munro, Glasgow, 10th Edition).

W. Lillie: "History of Middlesbrough" (Middlesbrough Council 1968).

Maps & Charts in the possession of Hartlepool Reference Library.

Local Newspapers:

Hartlepool Free Press.
South Durham Herald.
South Durham & Cleveland Mercury.
Stockton & Hartlepool Mercury.
Northern Daily Mail.

Technical Magazines, etc:

The Link (House Magazine of Richardsons, Westgarth Group)
The Engineer.
Syren & Shipping.
The Shipbuilder.
Annual Report & Accounts of Richardsons, Westgarth Group.
Prospectus on the formation of Richardsons, Westgarth Group.

Manuscript Sources:

W. E. Loveridge: "A History of Richardson, Westgarth of Hartlepool".

Acknowledgements

The author gratefully acknowledges the willing help and advice he has had from the following:

The staffs of Reference Libraries at Hartlepool, Middlesbrough and Newcastle upon Tyne: of Hartlepool & Hull Maritime Museums, the National Maritime Museum and Cochrane's Shipbuilders, Selby.

H. S. Appleyard, R. S. Bates, N. R. Neal, R. B. Booth, W. G. Brown, Rev. R. H. Bull, G. B. Butler, J. F. Clark, G. Cox, R. W. Craig, R. H. Dickens, W. Doyle, K. B. Eddison, R. Frank, D. G. Hutchinson, C. J. Jackson, T. P. Macklam, J. B. Mason, K. J. Middis (Richardsons, Westgarth Group), Dr. Brian Newman, J. H. Proud, R. J. F. Richardson, M. W. Shout, R. Sowler, B. G. Spaldin, W. Summers, J. R. Taylor, B. Threadkell, T. L. Walker, H. Williamson.

RULES & REGULATIONS
TO BE
OBSERVED
BY THE
WORKMEN
EMPLOYED BY
THOMAS RICHARDSON AT CASTLE EDEN
IRON WORKS.

1. On and after November 4th to February 8th the Bell will ring at half-past Six in the Morning, and Six in the Evening; on and after February 8th to November 4th, the Bell will ring at Six in the Morning and Six in the Evening, for a day's work—except on SATURDAYS, when the day's work will end at Four o'clock throughout the Year.

2. The half hour allowed for Breakfast to be, during the winter quarter, from half-past Eight o'clock to Nine : and during the remainder of the year from Eight to half-past Eight.

3. The second quarter to commence immediately after Breakfast throughout the year.

4. The aforesaid hours to apply to any man employed within the yard or on the premises ; and to work in the Shop, ~~xxxxxxxx~~ while it is dark. *during the winter quarter—*

NOTICE.

From January 1st, 1871, the following clause will be added to the Rules of these Works, viz.:--

That One Penny per Fortnight be deducted from every Man, and One Penny per Month from every Apprentice, employed in these Works, in aid of the Funds of the Hartlepool Hospital.

BY ORDER.

HARTLEPOOL IRON WORKS,
December 20th, 1870.

Hartlepool: J. PROCTER, Printer and Lithographer by Steam Power, Southgate. 16,227.

* Thomas RICHARDSON (CIR 1795)—(18 Oct 1850) m. (CIR 1820) Isabella HESLOP (CIR 1795)—(28 Mar 1835)

> Started as Timber Contractor for Earl of Durham. Opened Wingate & Castle Eden collieries. 1832 leased site at crossing of Stockton-Sunderland turnpike & H'pool Railway to start iron foundry & works. Lease expired 13.11.1853. C. Eden works ceased April 1853. (BGS) In 1837, with G. Parkin, built Hartlepool's 1st ship ("Castle Eden").

· * Margaret Ann RICHARDSON (CIR 1817)—(CIR 1819)
   (DAUGHTER)

· * Mary RICHARDSON (CIR 1819)—(9 Apr. 1892)

· * Thomas RICHARDSON (6 Jun. 1821)—(29 Dec. 1890) m. (2 Nov. 1843) Maria Anna Pearson GREENWELL (2 Sep. 1822)—(5 Feb. 1911)
   (SON)

> Shipbldr with JWR to 1857. Wife the daughter of a Sunderland ship-owner. T.R. in the Richardsons business at Hartlepool (Middleton), served apprenticeship under father. MP for Hartlepools 1874 briefly. Left Commons due financial problems. MP again 1880 and again 1886 to death. Rented The Friarage, Yarm 1863 from Thomas Meynell, moved to Kirklevington Grange 1873, and then built Kirklevington Hall, where he moved in 1884.

· · * Thomas RICHARDSON (28 Dec. 1846)—(22 May 1906) m. 30 Apr. 1879) Anna Constance COOKE-FABER (CIR 1859)—(CIR 1918)
   (GRAND SON)

> Freeman of West Hartlepool 1897. Knighted 1898. Educ. Rossall School & Cambridge (B.A.) 7 son & 2 daughters. Entered the business about 1868. NDM 1906 says first school of St. Peter's, York. Alderman, West H'pool Cncl. Chairman of Manchester & Salford S.S. Co. 1899— a Sivewright Bacon subsid. Lived at Kirklevington Grange.

· · · * Thomas RICHARDSON (17 Jan. 1880)—(20 Apr. 1956) m. (10 Sep. 1913) Winifred Ernestine TEMPLER (CIR 1890)—
   (GREAT GRAND SON)

> Called to Bar 1905. County Court Judge—Durham 1927, Northumberland and North Durham 1938. Retired 1953. Known as "The Friendly Judge" (NDM) Survived by 2 sons & 2 daughters.

· · · · * Thomas Templer RICHARDSON (22 Aug. 1914)—(14 May 1937)
   (GREAT-GREAT-GRAND SON)

> In R.A.F.V.R. Died landing with dead engine in soft sand at Seaham, Durham.

· · · · * Winifred Anna Blanche RICHARDSON (17 Dec. 1915)— m. (11 Sep. 1937) Cecil Gerard ALEXANDER
   (GREAT-GREAT-GRAND DAUGHTER)

· · · · * John David Benbow RICHARDSON (6 Apr. 1919)—
   (GREAT-GREAT-GRAND SON)

* Gladys Hebe Katharine RICHARDSON (4 Dec. 1920) — m. (21 Sep. 1957) Charles William WHITE
(GREAT-GREAT-GRAND DAUGHTER)

* Frederick Gordon Faber RICHARDSON (22 Jul 1930) —
(GREAT-GREAT-GRAND SON)

* Alice Constance RICHARDSON (10 Sep. 1881) — (2 Nov. 1969)
(GREAT-GRAND DAUGHTER)
Trained as artist by Seymour Lucas. Very capable flower and portrait painter. Exh. Royal Academy 1927-38. Member RA, Royal Soc. of Portrait Painters, Royal Institute Oil Painters. Also studied under Geo. Harcourt, and at Byam Shaw & Vicat Cole schools & Regent St. Polytechnic. (Dic. of British Artists 1880-1940 and RJFR). World War II Red Cross Commandant at St. Mary Abbott's Hosp. Kensington. Lived latterly 37 Bedford Gdns, Kens'ton.

* John Stanley RICHARDSON (29 Jun. 1883) — (28 Oct 1914) m. (18 Sep. 1913) Violet TEMPLER (CIR 1885) —
(GREAT-GRAND SON)
Capt. in Royal Engineers, serving in India when WWI started. Drafted to France, and 11 weeks later reported missing at Neuve Chappelle after an action in which most of his regiment was wiped out. Awarded Civil Dunbar Medal while serving in India, by Pres. Bombay Residency. Known as "Jack".

* Ernest Benbow RICHARDSON (25 Mar. 1885) — (28 Oct 1915)
(GREAT-GRAND SON)
Enlisted R.E. Jan. 1915 & sent to Suvla Bay as Corporal. Successfully sank 3 wells to supply water. Commissioned in field. Died of dysentery on way home. His sister Alice Constance later visited Suvla Bay & located his wells. Circa 1912 bought land at Windermere, British Columbia & cleared it to settle. Assisted for a time by brother Douglas. Returned to U.K. to join Army.

* Arthur Douglas RICHARDSON (1 Aug. 1886) — (12 Jan. 1915)
(GREAT-GRAND SON)
Joined West Yorks Regt. as 2nd Lieut. Trained in S. of England: died on leave at home of enteric fever. In 1913 travelled to British Columbia to work on brother Ernest Benbow's land. Crossed by "Teutonic" to Montreal, then train via Crow's Nest Pass, finally 4 days in 'buggy' @ 20 miles per day. Came back on outbreak of WWI.

* Leonard Faber RICHARDSON (5 Jun. 1889) — (2 Feb. 1912)
(GREAT-GRAND SON)
Naval Officer: served in "Hampshire" & "Hindustan". Lost aged 22 in HM Subm. A3 in a collision off Isle of Wight February 1912. Was in HMS "Venerable" for Naval Review for George V. Coronation (1910).

* Roland Charles RICHARDSON (12 Jun. 1891) — (26 Feb. 1968) m. (25 Jan. 1921) Freda BOANSON (17 Dec. 1900) — (6 Sep. 1967)
(GREAT-GRAND SON)
Educated Oatlands & Rossall '06-09. Trained as accountant (1914 @ Barrow). In West Yorks Regt. 1914-18. Captain, M.C. Later joined Boansons decorating business, H'pool.

Page 78

* Roland James Faber RICHARDSON (11 May 1923) — m. (8 Apr. 1953) Agnes Joan EDGAR (23 Jun. 1928) —
(GREAT-GREAT-GRAND SON)
Educated: Elleray Park School, Wallasey/Radley College, Berks. Apprentice in Cammell, Laird drawing office + Birkenhead Tech. Coll to HNC Naval Archit. Then business (Boanson's) in Hartlepool, retiring to York 1983.

* Evelyn Gladys RICHARDSON (3 Nov. 1893) — (14 Jun. 1912)
(GREAT-GRAND DAUGHTER)
Cause of death — complications from measles said to have been caught while on holiday at Aysgarth.

* Raymond De Dibon RICHARDSON (12 Feb. 1898) — (21 Mar. 1919)
(GREAT-GRAND SON)
Joined Navy age 17: awarded DSC at Suvla Bay. In "Royal Oak" at Jutland, and saw much other naval action. Death from 'Spotted Fever': said that whole ward of 20 young men died. (RJFR). Awarded DSC for services at Gallipoli (YP 15.3.1916). Attended Geo. V Coronation Review with Osborne Cadets.

* William John RICHARDSON (CIR 1848) —
(GRAND SON)
NDM 1890 states worked in the family business.

* Henry RICHARDSON (CIR 1850) — m. (CIR 1880) M. WARNES
(GRAND SON)
NDM 1890 states "living in Harrogate". Never in the engineering biz.

* Charles Edward RICHARDSON (5 Oct. 1953) — (16 Jan. 1940)
(GRAND SON)
NDM 1890 reports his being "recently" made Vicar of Redmarshall, Stockton. Previously at St. Pancras, London. Painter — Exhibited Royal Academy 1897-1909. Had studio in Kirklevington village. (RJFR). BA (Cantab) 1874 (So. Durham & Cleveland Mercury Sept 1874). Was the last Richardson to live in Kirklevington Hall.

* Alice RICHARDSON (CIR 1862) — (CIR 1928) m. (CIR 1885) Henric LEWIN
(GRAND DAUGHTER)

* Maria Dorothy LEWIN (CIR 1888) — m. (CIR 1917) C. T. McLEAN
(GREAT-GRAND DAUGHTER)

* Eleanor RICHARDSON (CIR 1862) — m. X. DOMVILLE
(GRAND DAUGHTER)

* George RICHARDSON (CIR 1823) — (9 Mar. 1855)
(SON)

* Margaret Isabel RICHARDSON (CIR 1825) — (CIR 1897) m. (CIR 1847) William ARMSTRONG (CIR 1823) —
(DAUGHTER)

* William ARMSTRONG (CIR 1848) — m. (CIR 1871) Eva DENTON (CIR 1849) —
(GRAND SON)

* Ralph RICHARDSON (CIR 1828) — (30 May 1858)
(SON)

* James RICHARDSON (CIR 1830) — (7 Apr. 1858)
(SON)

* John William RICHARDSON (CIR 1832) — (CIR 1884)
(SON)
1871 Census age 39, resident Seaton Carew. Died on visit (?) to London, age 52. Shipbuilder with father (to 1850) & brother Thomas (2) to 1857, then marine engine builder, etc.

Page 79

WANTED,

AS AN

APPRENTICE

TO A

COPPER SMITH,

A STOUT LAD

That has been some time at the Tin Smith Business.

APPLY TO

T. RICHARDSON & SONS,

June 11th, 1860.   Hartlepool Iron Works.

£5 REWARD.

☞ WILFUL DAMAGE. ☜

Whereas on Sunday the 30th April, some person or persons, at present unknown, did WILFULLY AND MALICIOUSLY DAMAGE several OFFICE DOORS at the Middleton Engine Works, the property of Messrs. Thos. Richardson & Sons.

The above Reward will be paid to any person giving such information as will lead to the detection and conviction of the offender or offenders on application to

A. WINTERBOTTOM,

CHIEF CONSTABLE.

Borough Police Office,
Hartlepool, 4th May, 1899.

F. W. Mason, Printer and Manufacturing Sta'   .rtlepool and West Hartlepool.

THE MARINE ENGINE OUTPUT OF THOMAS RICHARDSON & SONS, HARTLEPOOL 1851-1900

YEAR	SHIP	OFFNO	TONNA	BUILDER	YARD	TYPE	NHP	IHP	REMARKS
1851	Flying Dutchman ?	n.k.		G. Parkin, Sld		Simp.	30	-	Paddle-tug (Huntley)
1855	Sir Colin Campbell	n.k.	536 G	Richardson, Hpl	9	Simp.	70	-	8½ knots
1855	Killingworth / Skaato	26450	607 G	C. Mitchell, N/C	8	Simp.	70	-	See 1873 for NE (C2Cy) by TR.
1856	Florence Nightingale	14439	530 G	Richardson, Hpl	10	Simp.	90	-	
1856	Gipsy Queen	12889	670 G	M. Pearse	6	Simp.	100	-	see 1873 for re-engining.
1856	Ireland /Don Pedro	9384	974 G	Richardson, Hpl	13	Simp.	150	-	Jaffrey Patent
1856	Eider	9490	186 G	C.Lungley,Deptfd	-	Simp.	40	-	Re-boilered '73. N E Blair '71
1856	Victor Emmanuel	15684	540 G	Richardson, Hpl	11	Simp.	90	-	10 knots
1857	Ann	10140	360 D	Richardson, Hpl	15	Simp.	60	-	
1857	General Williams	n.k.	537 G	Richardson, Hpl	12	Simp.	90	-	
1857	Paulina / Vesta	Holland	400 G	Clavither, Danzig ?	-	Simp.	80	-	
1857	Londonderry	19475	412 G	John Pile, W. Hpl	8	Simp.	60	-	re-engined TR 1875, q.v.
1857	Armenian	30675	999 G	Richardson, Hpl	14	Simp.	100	-	8 k: 7½ cwt/hr. Patent engine.
1857	Reliance	20765	424 G	J.W.Hoby, Renfrew	-	Simp.	66	-	
1857	Middlesbrough / Lugar	19482	238 G	Richdsn Duck, Stkn	-	Simp.	40	-	re-boilered TR 1869
1858	Sarawak/Marco Bozzais	Greek	659 G	John Pile, W. Hpl	13	Simp.	120	-	
1858	Bobolina	25163	192 G	John Pile, W. Hpl	18	Simp.	80	-	
1858	La Ville de Dieppe	France	90 G	???, Belfast	-	Simp.	50	-	Side-lever. Paddle.
1858	Chow Phya	71507	600 R	John Pile, W. Hpl	11	Simp.	75	386	8T/day: 1.94-2.18 Lbs/IHP/Hr
1858	Attalante	Holland	294 G	John Pile, W. Hpl	17	Simp.	70	-	
1859	Matias-Cousino	Chile	877 G	A.Mitchell, N/c	-	C2Cy.	132	-	Date doubtful if Compound.
1859	Battasis	n.k.	450 B	John Pile, W. Hpl	22	Simp.	90	-	Wrecked 1864
1859	Guillermina	n.k.	425 G	Pile, Spence W.Hpl	25	Simp.	90	-	
1859	Tyamados	n.k.	452 B	John Pile, W. Hpl	21	Simp.	90	-	
1859	Montebello ?	n.k.		Richdsn Duck, Stktn	-	Simp.	120	-	
1860	Ann	28654	899 G	Richdsn Duck, Stktn	-	Simp.	130	-	
1860	Zaimis	28378	317 G	Richdsn Duck, Stktn	59	Simp.	45	-	
1860	Carolina ex Palikari	29393	1116G	Richdsn Duck, Stktn	-	Simp.	145	-	Later Comp. 2:26,45x27 140NHP
1860	Londos	28745	286 G	Richdsn Duck, Stktn	-	Simp.	45	-	
1860	Rangoon	28867	498 R	Pile, Spence W.Hpl	30	Simp.	120	-	
1861	Atlas	43757	846 G	J. Laing, Sld	36	Simp.	120	-	Len.1870 [1108G](L'pl U/w 72)
1861	Pet	28678	63 G	??? S.Shlds	-	Simp.	50	-	Wood.Paddle. MNL1871 30NHP
1861	Nina	Spain	799 G	Pile, Spence W.Hpl	-	Simp.	140	-	
1862	Lloyds	44831	941 G	Pile, Spence W.Hpl	39	Simp.	150	-	
1862	Shario Maru	Japan.	681 G	Oswald & Co., Sld	-	Simp.	120	-	ex Shaftesbury
1862	Tynemouth	43611	49 G	?? Sld	-	Simp.	90	-	Paddle-tug
1862	Princess	n.k.		Pile, Sld	-	Simp.	110	-	SOME DOUBT ABOUT THIS VSL.
1862	Elena	Spanish.	589 G	Richdsn Duck, Stktn	75	Simp.	90	-	
1862	Leda	45017	715 G	Richdsn Duck, Stktn	-	Simp.	90	-	
1862	Justitia		702 G	Richdsn Duck, Stktn	-	Simp.	120	-	
1862	Pet		233	Backhse & Dixon	1	Simp.	50	-	
1862	Corcyra /City of Cadiz	45019	734 G	Richdsn Duck, Stktn	90	Simp.	66	-	re-engined TR 1876
1863	Alexandra	45840	581 G	Richdsn Duck, Stktn	-	Simp.	90	-	re-boilered 1871.
1863	Princess Thyra	n.k.		Richdsn Duck, Stktn	-	Simp.	200	-	
1863	Clothilde	n.k.		Richdsn Duck, Stktn	-	Simp.	250	-	
1863	Tantah	Egypt.	1314G	Richdsn Duck, Stktn	-	Simp.	250	-	
1863	Morna	44951	833 G	Backhouse & Dixon	-	Simp.	175	-	New boiler 1868.
1863	Mona		693 G	Backhse & Dixon	-	Simp.	110	-	
1864	Elaine		593 G	Candlish Fox, Mbro	-	Simp.	90	-	
1864	Daira or Daria ?	n.k.	570 G	Backhouse, Mbro	-	Simp.	96	-	
1864	Granadian	49893	1718G	Pile, Spence W.Hpl	56	Simp.	200	-	MNL(1866) 300HP
1864	Uitenhage	Holland	1462G	J.Laing, Sld	59	Simp.	300	-	L'pool 1872 250NHP
1864	Alpha / Rosetta	49857	1261G	T. H. Pile, Hpl	1	Simp.	120	-	By 1874 N E by Earles, Hull

YEAR	SHIP	OFFNO	TONNA BUILDER	YARD	TYPE	NHP	IHP	REMARKS
1864	Damietta	50283	565 G Backhouse, Mbro	-	Simp.	90	-	
1864	Koina	51151	897 G Candlish Fox, Mbro	-	Simp.	120	-	
1864	Kaffraria	49917	859 G ??? S'ld	-	Simp.	120	-	L'pool Reg. 1872 (R.Craig)
1865	The Greek	52805	749 G Rich. D. Duck, Hpl	-	Simp.	140	-	
1865	Chrysolite	29934	702 G Candlish Fox, Mbro'	-	Simp.	100	-	
1865	Hansa	German	747 G Richdsn Duck, Stktn	-	Simp.	140	-	THIS VESSEL DOUBTFUL.
1865	Malacca/King of Greeks	54692	1684G R. D. Duck, H'pool	60	Simp.	300	-	
1865	Francoli	Spain	1038G J.Laing, Sld	67	Simp.	180	-	
1865	El Rahmanieh	Egypt.	1688G Richdsn Duck, Stktn	-	Simp.	300	-	
1865	York	54882	692 G F.Marshall, Shields	-	Simp.	90	-	
1865	Albany	n.k.	1371G J.Laing, S'ld	60	Simp.	250	-	(L'pl U/w 1872)
1865	Dessouk /Dolmebaktchi	Turkey ?	1389G Denton, Gray Hpl	56	Simp.	200	-	By 1890 N E W.Cramp,Philad'ia
1865	Wear	53083	750 G T.R.Oswald, Sld	46	Simp.	-	-	re-engined TR 1873
1865	Eptanisos ex Alora		Richardson Duck	-	Simp.	120	-	Built on spec. Launch 25/2/65
1866	Lady Alice Hill/Lubeck	n.k.	258 G Denton, Gray Hpl	65	Simp.	55	-	
1866	Galicia	54712	750 G R. D. Duck, Hpl	62	Simp.	98	-	80 rpm 11.75k
1866	Sunda	54737	1704G Backhouse, Mbro	-	Simp.	300	-	re-engined 1874
1866	Orion / Venus	Holland	373 G Richdsn Duck, Stktn	129	Simp.	130	-	
1866	Gado	n.k.	515 G R. D. Duck, Stocktn	112	Simp.	80	-	for Portuguese trade.
1866	Coumondouros	52806	1014G R. D. Duck, Stktn	109	Simp.	160	-	1867 owned TR:ex 'Dinsdale'
1866	Columbian	n.k.	2158R Pile, Spence W.Hpl	77	Simp.	200	-	By 1874 N E Maudslay, London
1867	Cristobal Colon/Savoie	n.k.	? Oswald & Co., Sld	-	Simp.	300	-	Blt. 1854. Len. 1867 Oswald.
1867	Bosphorus		943 G Denton,Gray Hpl	68	Simp.	110	-	Part blt. by Pile Spence Whpl
1867	Marion	56883	644 G Denton, Gray Hpl	71	Simp.	98	-	
1867	City of Buenos Aires	56884	1713G Richdsn Duck, Stktn	131	Simp.	250	-	Boilers athwartship.
1867	Astraea	Holland	523 G Richdsn Duck, Stktn	130	Simp.	90	-	re-engined & new boiler '76
1867	Britannia	13763	927 G W. Joyce,Greenwich	-	Simp.	130	-	Blt.1856 - Penn engines.
1867	Lizzie English	54570	673 G Denton, Gray Hpl	66	Simp.	96	-	
1867	Emma	France	780 G Denton, Gray Hpl	63	Simp.	130	-	built on spec. Sold 3/1868.
1867	Massowah/Borneo	n.k.	1770G Denton, Gray Hpl	64	Simp.	350	-	completed only 1868/9
1868	John Vaughan / Eleanor	63997	479 G Backh. & Dixon, Mbr	-	Simp.	80	-	
1868	Henry Brand	62756	706 G Denton, Gray Hpl	77	Simp.	90	-	
1868	Marmora	58753	930 G Denton, Gray Hpl	69	Simp.	230	-	Blair engines in LR 1874.
1868	Ebor	58754	705 G Denton, Gray Hpl	74	Simp.	96	-	
1868	Amy	58755	583 G Denton, Gray Hpl	76	Simp.	80	-	Lost 7.9.1868
1868	Raithwaite Hall	54573	698 G Denton, Gray Hpl	75	Simp.	90	-	see 1874 for re-engining.
1868	Eleanor		Backhse & Dixon	-	Simp.	80	-	n.k.
1868	Chow Phya	71507	507 G Pile, Spence W.Hpl	11	Simp.	70	-	Re-engined TR 1868. Blt 1858
1868	Vestor	Holland.	? , Holland	-	Simp.	70	-	11¼ knots
1869	Suez/G.N.Wilkinson	63032	675 G Denton, Gray Hpl	87	Simp.	98	-	
1869	Prima	German	520 G Denton, Gray Hpl	89	Simp.	80	-	
1869	Kepier	62549	703 G J. Laing, Sld	158	C2Cy.	90	-	
1869	Margaret / True Blue	60922	696 G Denton, Gray Hpl	80	Simp.	96	-	
1869	John Vaughan		-- Backh. & Dixon, Mbr	--	Simp.	80	-	
1869	William Banks	60933	722 G C.Mitchell, N/C	-	Simp.	98	-	T.R. Compound 24,38x30 later
1869	Alexander II	Russia	729 G Pile, Spence W.Hpl	29		70	-	1860 Simp.E. by J.Thompson,Sld
1869	Sandsend	54575	682 G Denton, Gray Hpl	79	Simp.	86	-	r-engined TR 1874
1869	Santos / St. Pauli	63266	961 G C. Mitchell, N/C	-	Simp.	96	-	L'pool 1872 120NHP
1869	Esk	58781	676 G Denton, Gray Hpl	83	Simp.	90	-	1876 N E by Geo. Clark (Comp.)
1869	Chance/Maria	63190	703 G Denton, Gray Hpl	88	Simp.	90	-	
1869	John Byng	63531	711 G C. Mitchell, N/C	-	Simp.	86	-	re-engined TR 1877 as Nordnaes
1869	Ouse	58780	705 G Denton, Gray Hpl	81	Simp.	90	-	
1870	Wessel/Albatross/Cymba	Norway	858 G Smith & Rodger G'gw	-	C2Cy.	90	-	Blt.1850: new TR engine 1870

YEAR	SHIP	OFFNO	TONNA	BUILDER	YARD	TYPE	NHP	IHP	REMARKS
1870	Arana	Spain	615 G	Backhouse, Mbro	-	C2Cy.	115	-	
1870	Rosa	65035	863 G	Denton, Gray Hpl	103	C2Cy.	98	-	LR(87) 944 GTons
1870	Amazon / Perseverant	63040	606 G	Withy, Alex., Hpl	9	Simp.	86	-	
1870	Moldavia	63255	698 G	Denton, Gray Hpl	92	C2Cy.	90	-	pd for by TR with 2 engines.
1870	Euxine/Gt.Northern	63584	1346G	Denton, Gray Hpl	91	C2Cy.	130	500	See 1892 for re-engining by TR
1870	Maude	63038	769 G	Denton, Gray Hpl	94	Simp.	90	360	25 s.ft HS/NHP.
1870	Bonita	63656	1886G	Backhouse, Mbro	-	C2Cy.	300	-	
1870	Cifuentes	Spain	673 G	Backhouse, Mbro	56	C2Cy.	115	-	re-engined TR 1880
1870	Shotton / Apollo	65034	754 G	Withy, Alex., Hpl	13	C2Cy.	96	-	
1870	Tom Pyman	65028	890 G	Denton, Gray Hpl	97	Simp.	99	-	
1870	Seafield	65029	642 G	Denton, Gray Hpl	99	C2Cy.	96	-	New Boiler 1878
1870	May /Julius Caesar	65026	856 G	Denton, Gray Hpl	96	Simp.	96	-	
1870	Secunda	German	665 G	Denton, Gray Hpl	101	Simp.	96	360	
1870	Magdala	63037	705 G	Withy, Alex., Hpl	10	Simp.	86	-	
1870	Dora / Pandora	65038	793 G	Denton, Gray Hpl	105	C2Cy.	96	-	New Boiler 1878.
1870	Said	62600	1060G	J. Laing, Sld	166	Simp.	100	-	
1870	Nina	n.k.	842 G	Richdsn Duck, Stktn	130	C2Cy.	-	-	Blt 1867. New E & B TR 1870
1870	Blyth	60554	1061G	Pile, S'ld	196	Simp.	98	-	(L'pl U/w 1872)
1870	Ann Webster / Londres	63689	771 G	Withy, Alex.	14	C2Cy.	96	-	Re-engined TR 1876
1870	Huelva	63677	752 G	Denton, Gray Hpl	102		90	-	
1870	Marg't Banks/Glenholm	63646	830 G	Denton, Gray Hpl	98	Simp.	96	-	re-engined TR 1878
1870	Mabel	63036	761 G	Denton, Gray	93	Simp.	96	360	Bunker Cap.120T
1870	Evora	63569	1717G	Pile, Sld	185	Simp.	250	-	Jaffrey Patent: 13¼ Tons/day
1870	Thomas Hampton	65036	821 G	Denton, Gray Hpl	104	C2Cy.	90	360	TR paid with 2 eng.
1870	George Lockett	63267	869 G	Backh. & Dixon, Mbr	-	C2Cy.	90	-	
1870	Ibex /Norway/Transport	65032	803 G	Withy, Alex., Hpl	12	C2Cy.	96	-	
1871	Emma Trechmann/Helling	58758	757 G	Withy, Alex., Hpl	16	C2Cy.	96	-	
1871	Isa	65510	1331G	M. Pearse, Stockton	109	C2Cy.	120	-	
1871	Hugh Streatfeild	62623	806 G	Short Bros, Sld	41	Simp.	98	-	
1871	Wallachia	65506	705 G	Denton, Gray Hpl	114	C2Cy.	96	-	
1871	Wave	67516	957 G	Denton, Gray Hpl	122	C2Cy.	99	400	
1871	E.S.Jobson	58763	1117G	Withy, Alex., Hpl	25	C2Cy.	110	-	
1871	Seaton	65505	949 G	Denton, Gray Hpl	111	C2Cy.	99	-	
1871	Lady Anne	62610	741 G	J. Laing, Sld	170	Simp.	90	-	
1871	Vendsyssel / Comeet	65232	768 G	Backh & Dixon, Mbr	-	C2Cy.	99	-	L'pl Reg. 1872 Cyl 27,50
1871	McLeod	65511	719 G	Denton, Gray Hpl	116	C2Cy.	96	-	
1871	Oceano	65610	1004G	Backh. & Dixon, Mbr	-	C2Cy.	99	-	
1871	Chester	65512	1089G	Withy, Alex., Hpl	21	C2Cy.	110	-	
1871	Wyberton	65659	1117G	Withy, Alex., Hpl	26	C2Cy.	110	-	
1871	Thomas Parker	62633	1152G	Short Bros, Sld	43	C2Cy.	98	-	
1871	James Groves	67518	939 G	Withy, Alex., Hpl	23	C2Cy.	98	-	
1871	Richmond	65631	1080G	Backhouse, Mbro	-	C2Cy.	150	-	
1871	Himalaya / Pars	65039	746 G	Withy, Alex., Hpl	15	C2Cy.	96	-	L'pool '72 Cyl 27,43 x 36
1871	Francoli	Spain	1038G	J. Laing, Sld	67	C2Cy.	160	-	Blt 1865: NE TR 1871.
1871	Edward Williams	65518	772 G	Denton, Gray Hpl	117	C2Cy.	97	-	
1871	Streatlam	65507	633 G	E. Withy, Hpool	20	C2Cy.	80	-	Spaldin shows Blair eng.
1871	Farnley Hall	65508	952 G	R. Irvine, W. Hpl	9	C2Cy.	98	-	
1871	Mont Cenis	France		Backhouse & Dixon	-		150	-	
1871	Djanik	Turkish	1046G	Backh'se & Dixon,Mb	-	C2Cy.	120	-	
1871	Ada	65517	565 G	Backhouse, Mbro	-	C2Cy.	95	-	sunk Humber 11.1.1872
1871	Mary / La Cartuja	63714	848 G	Denton, Gray Hpl	112	C2Cy.	96	-	LR 110 NHP
1871	Norton	65040		Backhouse, Mbro	-	C2Cy.	95	-	
1871	Stanley	65509	936 G	Denton, Gray Hpl	113	C2Cy.	99	-	

THOS. RICHARDSON MARINE ENGINES: 1851-1900

YEAR	SHIP	OFFNO	TONNA	BUILDER	YARD	TYPE	NHP	IHP	REMARKS
1871	Buckingham	65398	1046G	Backhouse & Dixon	-	C2Cy.	115	-	
1872	Nor	Norway.	1194G	Backh. & Dixon, Mbr	-	C2Cy.	150	-	
1872	Bellona	German	1098G	Denton, Gray Hpl	133	C2Cy.	110	-	
1872	Loch-na-Gar	65089	1079G	Duthie, Aberdeen	-	C2Cy.	110	-	
1872	Carl Christian	n.k.		Backhouse & Dixon	-	C2Cy.	150	-	
1872	Pearl	68371	1115G	Backh. & Dixon, Mbr	-	C2Cy.	150	-	
1872	Altona	68359	1819G	Backhouse, Mbro	-	C2Cy.	260	-	
1872	Tom Morton	65782	1400G	Morton, Leith	-	C2Cy.	150	-	
1872	Antelope / Coral Queen	1159	953 G	Hodgson & Son, L'pl	-	C2Cy.	-	-	Blt.1846. E '66 Samuelson Hull
1872	Lufra	67529	1366G	Denton, Gray Hpl	130	C2Cy.	120	-	
1872	Cornelia	67520	938 G	Denton, Gray Hpl	127	C2Cy.	99	-	
1872	Burlington	67526	839 G	W. Doxford, Sld	50	C2Cy.	90	-	
1872	Quarta	German	1131G	Denton, Gray Hpl	136	C2Cy.	110	495	
1872	Memphis	German	1557G	Withy, Alex., Hpl	34	C2Cy.	178	-	
1872	Penelope	68373	1251G	Backh. & Dixon, Mbr	84	C2Cy.	156	-	
1872	John Adamson	68871	1691G	Short Bros, Sld	54	C2Cy.	150	-	
1872	Lumley	62668	753 G	J.Blumer, Sld	-	C2Cy.	90	-	
1872	James Mason	65721	871 G	Backhouse, Mbro	-	C2Cy.	99	-	
1872	Joseph	63717	880 G	Denton, Gray Hpl	131	C2Cy.	90	-	
1872	Sandringham/Soria/	65439	1159G	Backh. & Dixon, Mbr	74	C2Cy.	120	-	
1872	Matilde/Yurre/Angeles	Spanish ?	402 G	T.Wingate, Glasgow	-	C2Cy.	76	-	Built 1865:new E TR 1872
1872	Karnak	German	1286G	Withy, Alex., Hpl	32	C2Cy:	120	-	
1872	Acadian	61157	931 G	Denniston, Sld	-	C2Cy.	100	-	
1872	Atalanta	German	1246G	Denton, Gray Hpl	132	C2Cy.	115	-	LR 120 NHP
1872	Tertia	German	981 G	Denton, Gray Hpl	124	C2Cy.	100	-	IHP guaranteed
1872	Messina	German	1001G	Denton, Gray Hpl	134	C2Cy.	110	495	
1872	Florence	67522	1020G	Withy, Alex., Hpl	27	C2Cy.	99	-	Foundered Lizard 15.4.1872
1873	Solway	67542	792 G	Withy, Alex., Hpl	40	C2Cy.	90	-	
1873	Anna	Bergen	1545G	Raylton Dixon, Mbro	-	C2Cy.	180	-	
1873	Kronprinz / Turgot	German.	1076G	Short Bros, Sld	56	C2Cy.	98	-	later Turgot (87069)
1873	Hellespont	68149	1330G	Raylton Dixon, Mbro	-	C2Cy.	170	-	
1873	Quinta	German	1277G	Denton, Gray Hpl	140	C2Cy.	120	510	
1873	Ibis / Likata	German	1550G	Withy, Alex., Hpl	37	C2Cy.	150	-	
1873	Free Lance	68299	1178G	Raylton Dixon, Mbro	89	C2Cy.	99	-	Lengthened 1879
1873	John Bramall	68296	1463G	M. Pearse, Stktn	126	C2Cy.	130	-	
1873	Mary Coverdale	58767	793 G	Withy, Alex., Hpl	39	C2Cy.	90	-	
1873	Berenice	Holland	732 G	Richdsn Duck, Stktn	102	C2Cy.	115	-	Blt 1864. New Engines 1873 TR
1873	Denderah	German	1530G	Withy, Alex., Hpl	35	C2Cy.	150	-	
1873	Chatsworth / Julian	68137	966 G	J.Softley, So.Shlds	88	C2Cy.	95	-	Built 1872.
1873	Isadora	Chile.	597 G	Backh. & Dixon, Mbr	-	C2Cy.	90	-	
1873	Kong Sverre	Bergen	2386G	Backhouse & Dixon	-	C2Cy.	300	-	
1873	Wear	53083	750 G	Oswald & Co., Sld	46	C2Cy.	90	-	Blt.1865. new TR engine '93.
1873	Killingworth / Skaato	26450	578 G	C.Mitchell, Walker	8	Simp.	70	-.	Blt. 1855
1873	Hampton /Limburg/Freja	68474	1567G	J.Blumer, Sld	26	C2Cy.	200	-	
1873	Freja	No.	1849G	J.Blumer, Sld	26	C2Cy.	150	-	ex Hampton.
1873	Gipsy Queen	12889	699 G	M.Pearse, Stockton	6	C2Cy.	100	-	Blt. 1856: N E TR 1873.
1874	Ashgar	n.k.		Short Bros, Sld	62 ?	-	-	-	?Marie Lorentzen.
1874	Palma	67560	1171G	E. Withy, Hpl	48	C2Cy.	110	-	
1874	Black Watch	70266	1458G	Raylton Dixon, Mbro	-	C2Cy.	130	-	
1874	Sunda ex Count Sponeck	54737	1704G	Backh & Dixon, Mbro	-	C2Cy.	280	-	Blt. 1865 New E & B 1874
1874	Jeannie	58770	1161G	E. Withy, Hpl	43	C2Cy.	120	-	
1874	Sexta	German	156 G	Wm. Gray, W.H'pl	144	C2Cy.	35	152	Ind.152.3 IHP 100psi
1874	Rhondda	70273	1007G	E. Withy, Hpl	46	C2Cy.	98	-	

Page 84

YEAR	SHIP	OFFNO	TONNA	BUILDER	YARD	TYPE	NHP	IHP	REMARKS
1874	Malacca	54692	1709G	Denton, Gray Hpl	60	C2Cy.	300	-	Blt. 1865. Re-engined TR 1874
1874	Madeline	67550	1321G	E. Withy, Hpl	44	C2Cy.	130	-	
1874	Coomassie / Patria	France.	1404G	Raylton Dixon, Mbro	-	C2Cy.	180	-	
1874	Torrington/Noord Holl.	70670	1946G	Raylton Dixon, Mbro	103	C2Cy.	220	-	LR 266 NHP
1874	Rokeby	67549	1132G	Withy, Alex., Hpl	42	C2Cy.	110	-	
1874	Sandsend	54575	711 G	Denton, Gray Hpl	79	C2Cy.	86	-	New engines by TR 1874.Blt '69
1874	Nith	67554	1127G	R. Irvine, W. Hpl	17	C2Cy.	110	-	
1874	Gazelle	63033	589 G	Withy Alexander,Hpl	2	C2Cy.	90	-	New engines TR. Blt 1869
1874	Renpor	67552	1325G	Short Bros, Sld	63	C2Cy.	120	-	
1874	Marie / Minerva	Germany	532 G	AG Vulcan, Stettin	41	C2Cy.	79	-	Blt. 1864. New Eng. TR 1874
1874	Milton	70602	1207G	E. Withy, Hpl	45	C2Cy.	125	-	
1874	British Queen	49808	710 G	T.H.Pile, Hpl	3	C2Cy.	120	-	Blt. 1865 (E by FH) E TR '74
1874	Royal Welsh	70278	1498G	Raylton Dixon, Mbro	-	C2Cy.	150	-	
1874	W. Harkess	73268	1228G	W.Harkess, M'bro.	111	C2Cy.	99	-	HNP=RHP
1874	Pardo	70880	1194G	E. Withy, Hpl	47	C2Cy.	140	-	
1874	Breeze	67557	1010G	E. Withy, Hpl	49	C2Cy.	99	-	
1874	Raithwaite Hall	54573	704 G	Denton, Gray Hpl	75	C2Cy.	96	-	new E & B TR 1874. NHP=RHP
1874	Silksworth / Pinnas	68912	1047G	Short Bros, Sld	65	C2Cy.	100	-	
1874	Glendale	67551	1144G	R. Irvine, W. Hpl	16	C2Cy.	110	-	
1874	Rose Middleton	72641	796 G	Wm. Gray, W.H'pl	145	C2Cy.	90	360	
1875	Rosa Mary	70122	1080G	Wm. Gray, W.H'pl	151	C2Cy.	110	495	LR(90) 99NHP
1875	Valetta	72644	1327G	Wm. Gray, W.H'pl	148	C2Cy.	120	-	
1875	Pyrrha	62533	1095G	T.R.Oswald, Sld	-	C2Cy.	99	-	Blt. 1869. N.E. TR '75
1875	Edgworth	62554	1022G	Backh'se & Dixon,Mb	-	C2Cy.	120	-	Blt.1869: TR engines 1875
1875	Para	72646	1105G	E. Withy, Hpl	54	C2Cy.	99	450	sunk 26/2/80
1875	Alabama ex Rangoon	29103	1818G	Palmer Bros.,Jarrow	-	C2Cy.	250	-	Blt. 1860: New E & B (TR) 1875
1875	Conatio	Germany	1041G	Wm. Gray, W.H'pl	146	C2Cy.	110	495	
1875	Aberfeldy	72642	1352G	E. Withy, Hpl	50	C2Cy.	120	-	
1875	Sarah Ann	70121	1370G	E. Withy, Hpl	51	C2Cy.	130	-	
1875	Standard	72647	1661G	Wm. Gray, W.H'pl	152	C2Cy.	180	-	LR(90) 150NHP
1875	August	Norway	1595G	Raylton Dixon, Mbro	-	C2Cy.	160	-	
1875	City of Dortmund	54640	758 G	Richdsn Duck, Stktn	111	C2Cy.	98	-	Blt. 1865.Lord Byron NE TR 75
1875	J.B.Eminson	68928	1031G	Short Bros, Sld	71	C2Cy.	99	-	
1875	Scots Greys	70700	1843G	Raylton Dixon, Mbro	-	C2Cy.	180	-	re-engined/tripled by TR 1889
1875	J.B.Walker/Norman Mon.	70432	1435G	Raylton Dixon, Mbro	114	C2Cy.	150	-	
1875	Lady Aline	68933	600 G	J. Laing, Sld	214	C2Cy.	95	-	
1875	Londonderry	19475	439 G	Pile, Spence W.Hpl	8	Simp.	60	-	Blt. 1857. Re-engined TR 1875
1875	Nellie Martin/Asturian	73266	1804G	Raylton Dixon, Mbro	-	C2Cy.	180	-	Later Asturiano.
1875	Rugenwalde / Castor	German.	513 G	Short Bros, Sld	69	C2Cy.	70	-	
1876	Bergen	Norway ?	1378G	Burm. & Wain, C'hgn	59		-	-	Blt. 1871. New boilers only TR
1876	Wolviston	72653	1357G	E. Withy, Hpl	58	C2Cy.	130	-	
1876	City of Glasgow/Meteor	53013	667 G	Backh & Dixon, Mbro	-	C2Cy.	99	-	Blt. 1864. New E & B 1876 TR
1876	La Felguera	Spanish	694 G	Raylton Dixon, Mbro	-	C2Cy.	110	-	
1876	Corcyra/City of Cadiz	45019	779 G	Richdsn Duck, Stktn	90	C2Cy.	99	-	Blt. 1862: New E & B 1876.
1876	Horsley	70123	1352G	E. Withy, Hpl	57	C2Cy.	120	-	
1876	William Banks	60933	722 G	C.Mitchell, N/C	-	C2Cy.	100	-	Blt. 1869: re-engined TR 1876
1876	Astraea	Holland	523 G	Richdsn Duck, Stktn	130	C2Cy.	90	-	Built 1867, q.v.
1876	Evelyn	70124	1350G	Wm. Gray, W.H'pl	162	C2Cy.	110	495	
1876	Winston / Naval	72654	1401G	Wm. Gray, W.H'pl	160	C2Cy.	136	-	New B. 1897
1876	Lord Elgin	70774	219 G	Richdsn Duck, Stktn	216	C2Cy.	70	-	Paddle.
1876	Ann Webster	63689	771 G	Withy, Alex., Hpl	14	C2Cy.	115	-	Blt. 1870. 1876 2nd T.R.eng.
1876	Kate Fawcett / Bertha	73637	1383G	E. Withy, Hpl	52	C2Cy.	130	-	
1876	Wiltshire / Norma	76937	534 G	E. Withy, Hpl	59	C2Cy.	70	-	

YEAR	SHIP	OFFNO	TONNA	BUILDER	YARD	TYPE	NHP	IHP	REMARKS
1876	Austin Friars / Urd	44555	1314G	J. Laing, Sld	91	C2Cy.	98	-	Blt 1868,new E 1876.LR 114NHP
1876	Richard Anning	72537	1132G	Raylton Dixon, Mbro	-	C2Cy.	99	-	
1876	Charlton	62547	1218G	Backhouse & D.,Mbro	-	C2Cy.	120	-	Blt.'69. New TR E & B 1876
1876	Captain McClure	72648	464 G	Edw. Lindsay, N/C	-	C2Cy.	80	-	
1876	Lord Mar	70775	213 G	Richdsn Duck, Stktn	217	C2Cy.	70	-	Paddle.
1876	Dronningen	Denmark	371 G	Raylton Dixon, Mbro	125	C2Cy.	130	-	Diagonal Engines: Paddle
1876	Hallamshire	72649	1358G	E. Withy, Hpl	56	C2Cy.	130	-	
1876	Anglian/City of Lisbon	47988	633 G	C.Lungley, Deptford	-	C2Cy.	98	-	Blt 1864: re-eng.12y old TR
1876	Garron Tower	68947	650 G	E. Withy, Hpl	60	C2Cy.	90	-	
1876	Kaiteur	73744	1254G	E. Withy, Hpl	61	C2Cy.	110	-	
1877	Valhalla	78406	1420G	Wm. Gray, W.H'pl	176	C2Cy.	120	-	LR(00) 142NHP
1877	Nordnaes ex John Byng	63531	743 G	C.Mitchell, Walker	-	C2Cy.	96	-	Blt. 1869. New eng. TR 1877
1877	Marquis of Lorne	60574	1019G	T.R.Oswald, Sld	101	C2Cy.	120	-	Blt. 1870. N E TR 1877
1877	Helmstedt	78403	1586G	E. Withy, Hpl	66	C2Cy.	140	-	
1877	George Fisher	77206	1275G	Richdsn Duck, Stktn	239	C2Cy.	120	-	
1877	Sicilian / Rollon	70785	1369G	E. Withy, Hpl	70	C2Cy.	150	-	
1877	Bull	76118	568 G	Raylton Dixon, Mbro	-	C2Cy.	80	-	
1877	City of Rotterdam	67799	884 G	Richdsn Duck, Stktn	234	C2Cy.	120	-	
1877	Bear	76119	593 G	Raylton Dixon, Mbro	-	C2Cy.	80	-	
1877	Pierremont	72659	1278G	Wm. Gray, W.H'pl	167	C2Cy.	138	-	LR(90) 120NHP
1877	Zanzibar	72664	2245G	Wm. Gray, W.H'pl	169	C2Cy.	180	-	
1877	Yarm	70126	1248G	Wm. Gray, W.H'pl	172	C2Cy.	125	540	
1877	Tintern Abbey	77194	1223G	E. Withy, Hpl	63	C2Cy.	110	-	
1877	City of Amsterdam	77386	841 G	Richdsn Duck, Stktn	234	C2Cy.	120	-	
1877	Telesilla	76943	1233G	E. Withy, Hpl	62	C2Cy.	120	-	
1877	Horden / Kaethe	72658	1479G	Wm. Gray, W.H'pl	165	C2Cy.	140	-	LR Cyl 28½,58½ 176NHP
1877	Melita	72657	1390G	Wm. Gray, W.H'pl	164	C2Cy.	120	-	
1877	Blenheim	77038	1163G	E. Withy, Hpl	69	C2Cy.	99	-	
1877	Amanda / Eva	70127	1261G	Wm. Gray, W.H'pl	174	C2Cy.	110	-	re-boilered 1898.
1877	Overyssel	Holland	2168G	Raylton Dixon, Mbro	-	C2Cy.	220	-	
1877	Staincliffe / Roald	72663	1337G	M.Pearse, Stockton	154	C2Cy.	120	-	LR(00) 132 NHP
1877	James Groves	78404	1275G	Wm. Gray, W.H'pl	173	C2Cy.	99	-	LR(90) gives Cyl 27,50x33
1877	Wyberton / Zeeland	77045	2033G	Raylton Dixon, Mbro	-	C2Cy.	220	-	12 knots LR 245 NHP
1877	Scotsman/Marlboro'	76991	1827G	E. Withy, Hpl	64	C2Cy.	200	-	O/No 1887LR 76985
1877	Halcyon	70128	1586G	Raylton Dixon, Mbro	-	C2Cy.	140	-	
1878	March'ness of Lond'rry	68966	706 G	E. Withy, Hpl	71	C2Cy.	90	-	
1878	Hart	70129	1367G	Wm. Gray, W.H'pl	180	C2Cy.	120	-	
1878	Swiftsure	79632	1927G	Raylton Dixon, Mbro	-	C2Cy.	180	-	
1878	Marg't Banks /Glenholm	63646	826 G	Denton, Gray Hpl	98	C2Cy.	96	-	Blt. 1870. New E & B TR 1878
1878	Gertrude	70130	1370G	Wm. Gray, W.H'pl	197	C2Cy.	150	-	LR 180 NHP
1878	Rugby / Fanni	79653	1690G	Wm. Gray, W.H'pl	192	C2Cy.	150	-	
1878	Circassia	78414	1380G	Wm. Gray, W.H'pl	185	C2Cy.	120	-	
1878	Oakdale	77091	1408G	E. Withy, Hpl	72	C2Cy.	130	-	LR(95) 156 NHP
1878	Sowerby	78422	1254G	Wm. Gray, W.H'pl	194	C2Cy.	110	-	
1878	Dahomey	Ru.	1044G	Richdsn Duck, Stktn	245	C2Cy.	150	-	
1878	Crimdon	78410	1710G	Wm. Gray, W.H'pl	181	C2Cy.	170	-	
1878	Harlsey	78423	1729G	Wm. Gray, W.H'pl	195	C2Cy.	150	-	
1878	G.M.B.	76123	579 G	Raylton Dixon, Mbro	146	C2Cy.	90		
1878	Matthew Curtis	77215	1950G	E. Withy, Hpl	67	C2Cy.	180	-	LR (90) 200 NHP
1878	Elpis	78417	2010G	Wm. Gray, W.H'pl	189	C2Cy.	200	-	LR 180 NHP
1878	Gelderland	Holland	2173G	Raylton Dixon, Mbro	-	C2Cy.	200	-	
1878	Anatolia	78409	1662G	Wm. Gray, W.H'pl	179	C2Cy.	150	-	
1878	Hathersage	78420	1598G	Wm. Gray, W.H'pl	198	C2Cy.	178	-	LR (90) 150 NHP

YEAR	SHIP	OFFNO	TONNA	BUILDER	YARD	TYPE	NHP	IHP	REMARKS
1878	Moidart	80425	1293G	E. Withy, Hpl	77	C2Cy.	130	-	LR(00) 156NHP
1878	Hudson	78419	1630G	Wm. Gray, W.H'pl	193	C2Cy.	150	-	
1878	Valund	76873	705 G	E. Withy, Hpl	73	C2Cy.	105	-	
1878	Sherborne / Fagerheim	77033	1645G	E. Withy, Hpl	68	C2Cy.	150	-	
1878	Topaze	79664	1895G	C.S.Swan & Co. N/C	39	C2Cy.	180	-	
1878	Roumania	81501	1385G	Wm. Gray, W.H'pl	196	C2Cy.	120	-	
1878	Nicosian	79152	1360G	E. Withy, Hpl	78	C2Cy.	130	-	
1878	Wilton	78412	1575G	Wm. Gray, W.H'pl	182	C2Cy.	178	-	
1878	Annandale	79635	1521G	E. Withy, Hpl	75	C2Cy.	167	-	
1878	Netley Abbey	79383	1650G	Wm. Gray, W.H'pl	186	C2Cy.	180	-	
1878	Chamois	78416	1382G	E. Withy, Hpl	76	C2Cy.	130	-	
1878	Jeranos	79020	1979G	Richdsn Duck, Stktn	242	C2Cy.	235	-	
1878	Chicago	78411	1384G	Wm. Gray, W.H'pl	184	C2Cy.	140	-	
1878	Strathmore	78619	2138G	Raylton Dixon, Mbro	-	C2Cy.	250	-	
1878	Tom Pyman	65028	971 G	Denton, Gray Hpl	97	C2Cy.	99	-	Blt.'70. TR Conv. to C2Cy '78
1879	City of Dublin	81426	1146G	E. Withy, Hpl	80	C2Cy.	150	-	
1879	Pallion	78424	1723G	Wm. Gray, W.H'pl	199	C2Cy.	150	-	Tripled TR 1892 q.v.
1879	Roraima	79689	1178G	E. Withy, Hpl	79	C2Cy.	99	-	
1879	Hartville	81504	1674G	Wm. Gray, W.H'pl	206	C2Cy.	150	-	
1879	Halo	81652	1428G	E. Withy, Hpl	81	C2Cy.	120	-	
1879	Potaro / F.Bischoff	81572	1181G	E. Withy, Hpl	82	C2Cy.	131	-	
1879	Morven	82283	1365G	E. Withy, Hpl	84	C2Cy.	130	-	
1879	Captain Cook	58783	247 G	W.B.Hornby N/C	-	C2Cy.	50	-	Blt 1870. New E by TR 1879
1879	Consent	69000	1478G	Bartram Haswell,Sld	103	C2Cy.	140	-	
1879	Mennythorpe	81651	1701G	Wm. Gray, W.H'pl	200	C2Cy.	150	675	
1879	Mabel	81653	1116G	Wm. Gray, W.H'pl	208	C2Cy.	99	-	
1879	Beatrice	81209	1385G	Turnbull, Whitby	66	C2Cy.	140	-	
1879	Chilton	81502	1118G	Wm. Gray, W.H'pl	203	C2Cy.	99	450	
1879	Eden	81503	1446G	Wm. Gray, W.H'pl	204	C2Cy.	120	-	
1879	Craiglands	78425	1113G	Wm. Gray, W.H'pl	201	C2Cy.	99	450	
1879	Carolina	80558	234 G	E. Withy, Hpl	85	C2Cy.	47	-	
1879	Bristol City	78460	1722G	Richdsn Duck, Stktn	256	C2Cy.	180	-	636th Marine Engine.(M.E.'79)
1879	Cymbeline / Louise	79470	1359G	Richdsn Duck, Stktn	252	C2Cy.	130	-	LR 145 NHP
1879	Salient	81456	1477G	Bartram Haswell,Sld	105	C2Cy.	140	-	
1879	New York City /Braila	78461	1724G	Richdsn Duck, Stktn	255	C2Cy.	180	-	New Boilers '84
1879	Captain Parry	67800	477 G	Richdsn Duck, Stktn	231	C2Cy.	80	-	Blt.1877. New E & B 1879
1879	Dalbeattie	76130	1395G	Raylton Dixon, Mbro	155	C2Cy.	120	-	
1879	Lucent	81453	1476G	Bartram Haswell,Sld	104	C2Cy.	140	-	LR(04) 167NHP
1879	Wolviston	81506	1785G	Wm. Gray, W.H'pl	207	C2Cy.	150	-	
1879	Jane	81211	1387G	Turnbull, Whitby	67	C2Cy.	140	-	LR 156 NHP
1880	Eident	81464	1586G	Short Bros, Sld	103	C2Cy.	150	-	
1880	Bath City	78462	1724G	Richdsn Duck, Stktn	256	C2Cy.	180	-	
1880	Sapphire	82824	2081G	Richdsn Duck, Stktn	264	C2Cy.	190	-	
1880	Sandal	81517	1760G	Wm. Gray, W.H'pl	218	C2Cy.	150	-	
1880	Tangier	81645	1908G	Raylton Dixon, Mbro	-	C2Cy.	210	-	
1880	Ingerid	Holland	640 G	Raylton Dixon, Mbro	-	C2Cy.	70	-	
1880	George Gowland	81620	593 G	Ramage,Ferguson,Lth	-	C2Cy.	95	-	
1880	Montgomeryshire	82827	1929G	Raylton Dixon, Mbro	-	C2Cy.	250	-	
1880	Stranton	81508	1754G	Wm. Gray, W.H'pl	213	C2Cy.	150	-	Tripled by TR 1892 (?1888)
1880	Hilda	81518	1761G	Wm. Gray, W.H'pl	222	C2Cy.	178	-	
1880	Cifuentes	Sp.	673 G	Backh'se & Dixon,Mb	56	C2Cy.	130	-	Blt. 1870: new TR engines '80
1880	Kaiser	81513	816 G	Wm. Gray, W.H'pl	217	C2Cy.	130	-	
1880	Cholmley	82663	1355G	Turnbull, Whitby	70	C2Cy.	140	-	

YEAR	SHIP	OFFNO	TONNA	BUltDER	YARD	TYPE	NHP	IHP	REMARKS
1880	Seaham Harbour	81479	1911G	E. Withy, Hpl	90	C2Cy.	182	-	
1880	Umballa ex Tangier	81645	1911G	Raylton Dixon, Mbro	-	C2Cy.	210	-	
1880	Muriel	76132	1384G	Raylton Dixon, Mbro	-	C2Cy.	120	-	
1880	Virent	81470	1676G	Short Bros, Sld	105	C2Cy.	160	-	
1880	Hardwick / Lizzie	81523	1122G	E. Withy, Hpl	92	C2Cy.	99	-	LR 120 NHP
1880	Scotsman / Tunis	82016	1682G	E. Withy, Hpl	91	C2Cy.	150	-	
1880	Titania	81339	1961G	Raylton Dixon, Mbro	-	C2Cy.	170	-	
1880	Utrecht	Holland	2227G	Raylton Dixon, Mbro	-	C2Cy.	200	-	
1880	Oakville	81467	1340G	Wm. Gray, W.H'pl	210	C2Cy.	120	-	
1880	Cyanus	82803	1635G	E. Withy, Hpl	80	C2Cy.	150	-	
1880	Blackhalls	81516	1142G	Wm. Gray, W.H'pl	219	C2Cy.	99	-	
1880	Parklands / Thyra	81511	1547G	Wm. Gray, W.H'pl	215	C2Cy.	159	-	
1880	Hartlepools	81507	1754G	Wm. Gray, W.H'pl	211	C2Cy.	150	-	
1881	City of Antwerp	n.k.	731 G	J. Blumer, S'ld	65 ?	C2Cy.	120	-	
1881	Jacob Christensen	Norway.	1763G	Raylton Dixon, Mbro	189	C2Cy.	160	-	
1881	Iron Acton / Patience	83897	1148G	Raylton Dixon, Mbro	-	C2Cy.	99	-	
1881	Billow	84527	1658G	E. Withy, Hpl	97	C2Cy.	160	-	
1881	Ranee/Labuan/Pin Seng	82865	617 G	Ramage Ferg'n,Leith	27	C2Cy.	99	-	NHP=RHP
1881	Gloucester City	85802	1940G	Richdsn Duck, Stktn	281	C2Cy.	200	-	
1881	Juliet	84111	2090G	Raylton Dixon, Mbro	-	C2Cy.	250	-	Year of build uncertain.
1881	Rocklands	84530	952 G	Irvine & Co., W.Hpl	37	C2Cy.	105	-	
1881	Zuid Holland	Holland	2276G	Raylton Dixon, Mbro	191	C2Cy.	220	-	
1881	Moggie	81657	1110G	E. Withy, Hpl	94	C2Cy.	99	-	
1881	Minard Castle	85115	2650G	Raylton Dixon, Mbro	-	C2Cy.	350	-	
1881	Lemuria / Artemisia	82898	1589G	E. Withy, Hpl	98	C2Cy.	187	-	
1881	Talley Abbey / Frigga	84659	958 G	Irvine & Co., W.Hpl	36	C2Cy.	100	-	
1881	Ravensdale	82851	1114G	E. Withy, Hpl	93	C2Cy.	110	-	LR(00) 134NHP
1881	Brenda/Alexander Shuk.	84522	1679G	E. Withy, Hpl	95	C2Cy.	150	-	
1881	Anjer Head / Pakshan	82893	2015G	Raylton Dixon, Mbro	182	C2Cy.	240	-	
1881	Westergate	85063	1794G	Short Bros, Sld	119	C2Cy.	160	-	LR(00) 198NHP
1881	Brooklyn City	78467	1726G	Richdsn Duck, Stktn	271	C2Cy.	180	-	
1881	Sharon	82670	1382G	Turnbull, Whitby	75	C2Cy.	130	436	
1881	Marima	85066	1672G	E. Withy, Hpl	100	C2Cy.	150	-	
1881	Chancellor	82755	2116G	Raylton Dixon, Mbro	-	C2Cy.	170	-	
1881	Hasland	84529	1755G	Wm. Gray, W.H'pl	237	C2Cy.	150	-	
1881	City of Hamburg	81436	1174G	J. Laing, Sld	269	C2Cy.	150	-	
1881	Uppingham	85046	2220G	Raylton Dixon, Mbro	-	C2Cy.	200	-	
1881	Harvest	84524	1380G	Irvine & Co., W.Hpl	35	C2Cy.	130	-	
1881	Coningsby	84534	1757G	Wm. Gray, W.H'pl	238	C2Cy.	150	-	
1881	Bothwell Castle	82872	2542G	Raylton Dixon, Mbro	180	C2Cy	300	-	
1881	Boyne	85047	2006G	Wm. Gray, W.H'pl	234	C2Cy.	200	-	
1881	Penang	82853	623 G	Ramage Ferguson,Lth	26	C2Cy.	120	-	
1881	Raisby	85090	2288	Short Bros., S'ld	118	C2Cy.	220	-	
1881	Lindus	85085	1697G	E. Withy, Hpl	101	C2Cy.	160	-	
1881	Beneficent	84996	2024G	Short Bros., S'ld	120	C2Cy.	100	-	see 1887 for re-engining.
1882	Silksworth	85020	1347G	E. Withy, Hpl	111	C2Cy.	140	-	
1882	Ingram	87001	1748G	E. Withy, Hpl	112	C2Cy.	150	-	LR 178 NHP
1882	Preston	84548	2539G	Wm. Gray, W.H'pl	256	C2Cy.	300	-	Lost 3/1/1885.
1882	Stanhope	86941	1366G	Irvine & Co., W.Hpl	42	C2Cy.	130	-	
1882	Burns	85197	2193G	E. Withy, Hpl	109	C2Cy.	240	-	Wrecked 7/10/1885
1882	Kronprinz	n.k.		Short Bros., S'ld	131	C2Cy.			
1882	Highgate	82677	1395G	Turnbull, Whitby	79	C2Cy.	130	-	
1882	Noord Brabant	Holland	2493G	Raylton Dixon, Mbro	-	C2Cy.	240	-	

YEAR	SHIP	OFFNO	TONNA	BUILDER	YARD	TYPE	NHP	IHP	REMARKS
1882	Watlington	86940	1814G	Wm. Gray, W.H'pl	260	C2Cy.	200	-	
1882	Morning Star	84544	1121G	Irvine & Co., W.Hpl	40	C2Cy.	99	-	
1882	Wellfield / Bestevaer	86939	1725G	E. Withy, Hpl	110	C2Cy.	211	-	
1882	Everilda	84677	1401G	Turnbull, Whitby	80	C2Cy.	130	-	
1882	Wordsworth	87010	2058G	Wm. Gray, W.H'pl	262	C2Cy.	224	-	
1882	Catanian	84929	2015G	E. Withy, Hpl	102	C2Cy.	200	-	
1882	Jersey City	85803	1936G	Richdsn Duck	285	C2Cy.	218	-	
1882	Hypatia	84547	2011G	E. Withy, Hpl	108	C2Cy.	200	-	
1882	Roehampton	85168	2143G	E. Withy, Hpl	107	C2Cy.	180	-	LR(00) 224NHP
1882	Jeanie	81660	1816G	E. Withy, Hpl	105	C2Cy.	180	-	LR 211 NHP
1882	Newcastle City	86943	2129G	E. Withy, Hpl	113	C2Cy.	220	-	
1882	Laura	84536	1123G	Irvine & Co., W.Hpl	38	C2Cy.	99	-	
1882	Scrivia	Italy	2542G	Raylton Dixon, Mbro	200	C2Cy.	284	-	
1882	Dewdrop	84540	1143G	Irvine & Co., W.Hpl	39	C2Cy.	100	-	
1882	City of Bristol	81439	1293G	E. Withy, Hpl	104	C2Cy.	150	-	
1882	Cousins Arbib	87042	2147G	Raylton Dixon, Mbro	209	C2Cy.	170	-	
1882	Constance	86936	1117G	Irvine & Co., W.Hpl	41	C2Cy.	100	-	
1882	Llandaff City	85806	1936G	Richdsn Duck	287	C2Cy.	224	-	
1882	Carib / Ivanhoe	84642	1437G	Richdsn Duck, Stktn	291	C2Cy.	99	-	
1882	Hawarden	84537	1816G	Wm. Gray, W.H'pl	247	C2Cy.	180	-	
1882	Joseph Arbib	85123	2139G	Raylton Dixon, Mbro	193	C2Cy.	170	-	
1882	Welbury	84542	1847G	Wm. Gray, W.H'pl	252	C2Cy.	160.	-	LR(00) 198NHP
1882	Turquoise	85117	2077G	Richdsn Duck, Stktn	284	C2Cy.	200	-	
1882	Essex	82758	2564G	Raylton Dixon, Mbro	194	C2Cy.	250	-	
1883	Atalanta	89454	1164G	Wm. Gray, W.H'pl	284	C2Cy.	160	-	
1883	Gjeilo	Norway.		Raylton Dixon, Mbro	-	C2Cy.	-	-	7 knots
1883	Kirtle	86953	1462G	E. Withy, Hpl	118	C2Cy.	130	-	
1883	Mary Lohden	86957	1363G	Irvine & Co., W.Hpl	45	C2Cy.	130	-	LR 156 NHP
1883	Ackworth	86947	1886G	Wm. Gray, W.H'pl	268	C2Cy.	160	-	Stranded 11/1885
1883	Primate	82764	1829G	Raylton Dixon, Mbro	208	C2Cy.	178	-	
1883	Luneburg	86972	1067G	J.Blumer, Sld	81	C2Cy.	99	-	
1883	China / Concordia	87905	2151G	E. Withy, Hpl	124	C2Cy.	200	-	
1883	Robina / Ellewoutsdyk	86643	1697G	J.L.Thompson, Sld	197	C2Cy.	167	-	
1883	Coventry	86973	1736G	E. Withy, Hpl	122	C2Cy.	150	-	
1883	Kennett	87171	1795G	E. Withy, Hpl	125	C2Cy.	160	-	
1883	Cogent	87351	2140G	Short Bros, Sld	142	C2Cy.	211	-	
1883	Mennythorpe	86384	1436G	Irvine & Co., W.Hpl	43	C2Cy.	130	-	LR 156 NHP
1883	Spyridion Vagliano	Greek.	1708G	Bartram Haswell,Sld	126	C2Cy.	170	-	
1883	City of Truro	86129	1767G	Wm. Gray, W.H'pl	282	C2Cy.	160.	-	LR 150 NHP
1883	Duchess	89452	1097G	E. Withy, Hpl	126	C2Cy.	156	-	
1883	Chelona	87331 ?	1675G	Bartram Haswell,Sld	142	C2Cy.	160	-	
1883	Maude / Melanie	86952	1693G	Wm. Gray, W.H'pl	270	C2Cy.	150	-	LR (90) 167 NHP
1883	Phoenix / Aarstein	87128	1783G	N.of E. S/B Co.,Sld	104	C2Cy.	160	-	
1883	March	86645	1969G	Turnbull, Whitby	92	C2Cy.	198	-	
1883	Renpor	86949	1917G	E. Withy, Hpl	117	C2Cy.	200	-	Sunk 1887·
1883	Aurora	86969	1718G	Raylton Dixon, Mbro	-	C2Cy.	180	-	
1883	Hermon	88901	1461G	E. Withy, Hpl	127	C2Cy.	130	-	
1883	Myrtle Branch	87348	1653G	Bartram Haswell,Sld	127	C2Cy.	167	-	
1883	Romeo	87922	2279G	Raylton Dixon, Mbro	-	C2Cy.	300	-	
1883	Fylingdale	86650	1657G	J.L.Thompson, Sld	198	C2Cy.	150	-	
1883	Chigwell	89491	1824G	Bartram Haswell,Sld	129	C2Cy.	200	-	
1883	Wandle	89490	1783G	E. Withy, Hpl	123	C2Cy.	150	-	
1883	Craiglands / Oresund	89456	1322G	Irvine & Co., W.Hpl	49	C2Cy.	156	-	

THOS. RICHARDSON MARINE ENGINES: 1851-1900

YEAR SHIP	OFFNO	TONNA BUILDER	YARD	TYPE	NHP	IHP	REMARKS
1883 Alcester	81777	1615G Richdsn Duck, Stktn	299	C2Cy.	180	-	
1883 Aboraca	86109	2129G Short Bros, Sld	141	C2Cy.	180	-	
1883 Agenoria	86974	1306G Irvine & Co., W.Hpl	47	C2Cy.	130	-	
1883 Gledholt	86954	1689G E. Withy, Hpl	119	C2Cy.	199	-	
1883 Ranmoor	87145	2113G E. Withy, Hpl	121	C2Cy.	224	-	
1883 Bellcairn	86950	1363G Irvine & Co., W.Hpl	44	C2Cy.	130	-	
1883 Raylton Dixon	Norway	1771G Raylton Dixon, Mbro	221	C2Cy.	198	-	
1883 Harrogate / Freja	87174	2116G Short Bros, Sld	146	C2Cy.	200	-	
1883 Welcombe	89524	2166 Raylton Dixon, Mbro	--	C2Cy.	170	-	
1883 Tourmaline	87075	2043G Richdsn Duck, Stktn	289	C2Cy.	200	-	
1883 Northern Star	89455	1175G Swan Hunter, Nwc	-	C2Cy.	107	-	
1883 Troqueer	86962	1360G Irvine & Co., W.Hpl	46	C2Cy.	130	-	
1884 Jacata /Lipsos/Gothia	Holland	2381G Raylton Dixon, Mbro	225	T3Cy.	202	-	
1884 William Adamson	90302	1955G Short Bros, Sld	160	C2Cy.	192	-	LR(00) 224NHP
1884 Rosehill	89773	1649G J.L.Thompson, Sld	201	C2Cy.	150	-	
1884 Albert	Norway	742 G Oscarshamn M.V.	-	C2Cy.	95	-	Engines made 1876 (LR '90-91)
1884 Longnewton	90309	1878G E. Withy, Hpl	133	T3Cy.	174	-	
1884 Lincoln City / Chicago	89467	2729G Wm. Gray, W.H'pl	289	C2Cy.	300	-	
1884 Chester	90357	1128G E. Withy, Hpl	131	T3Cy.	110	-	
1884 Aeolus	89470	1772G Wm. Gray, W.H'pl	291	C2Cy.	150	-	Sunk 6/8/1886
1884 Ashton	90365	990 G E. Withy, Hpl	132	T3Cy.	241	-	
1884 Fortunatus	89464	1306G Irvine & Co.,.W.Hpl	51	C2Cy.	156	-	10 knots
1884 Bala	89193	2014G Wm. Gray, W.H'pl	294	C2Cy.	175	-	
1884 Para	89539	1790G E. Withy, Hpl	129	T3Cy.	150	-	T.R. first Triple
1884 Gothenburg City	89465	2529G E. Withy, Hpl	130	C2Cy.	300	-	
1884 James Westoll	87375	1969G Short Bros, Sld	159	C2Cy.	192	-	
1884 Wivenhoe / Vera	89461	1893G Wm. Gray, W.H'pl	288	C2Cy.	170	675	LR(00) 198NHP
1884 Vane Tempest	90313	689 G E. Withy, Hpl	134	C2Cy.	90	-	
1884 Saltburn/Colac	89469	1479G E. Withy, Hpl	128	C2Cy.	140	-	
1884 Southwold / Cairnmona	89533	1766G Short Bros, Sld	156	C2Cy.	192	-	
1884 Herschel	89801	1783G Bartram Haswell,Sld	131	C2Cy.	178	-	
1884 Lizzie	88902	1351G Irvine & Co., W.Hpl	50	T3Cy.	130	-	
1884 Capulet	87956	2246G Raylton Dixon, Mbro	-	C2Cy.	300	-	
1885 Chelydra	91889	2467G J.L.Thompson, Sld	209	T3Cy.	300	-	
1885 Kaisow /Matsuyama Maru	91898	2959G J.L.Thompson, Sld	212	T3Cy.	600	-	LR 130psi 3160 GRT
1885 Shakespear	91869	1851G J.L.Thompson, Sld	210	T3Cy.	185	-	
1885 Heliades	91254	2965G Richdsn Duck, Stktn	319	T3Cy.	350	-	
1885 Derwent	n.k.	417 G Wm. Gray, W.H'pl	298	C2Cy.	70	350	
1885 Greystoke	89473	2119G E. Withy, Hpl	136	T3Cy.	160	-	
1885 Beresford / Nor	89474	2158G E. Withy, Hpl	138	T3Cy.	170	-	
1885 Stella	92903	2430G E. Withy, Hpl	140	T3Cy.	225	-	
1885 Ching Wo /Wakanoura M.	89689	2400G Raylton Dixon, Mbro	239	T3Cy.	400	-	
1885 J.M.Smith	90326	2055G Short Bros, Sld	158	T3Cy.	195	-	
1885 Algoma	91241	2914G J.L.Thompson, Sld	205	T3Cy.	300	-	
1885 Wells City / Progreso	85819	1958G N. of Eng.S/B, Sld	110	T3Cy.	195	-	
1885 Washington City / Fram	92901	2296G E. Withy, Hpl	137	T3Cy.	200	-	
1885 Anglian	68820	2274G Aitken Mansell, Ggw	60	T3Cy.	309	-	Blt. 1873.Conv.to T3Cy TR '85
1885 Bempton	89685	2013G E. Withy, Hpl	135	C2Cy.	170	-	
1885 Raphael	91858	1860G J.L.Thompson, Sld	208	C2Cy.	160	-	
1886 Federation	91963	2472G J.L.Thompson, Sld	214	T3Cy.	300	-	
1886 Pluto	Aust/Hung	186 G J.L.Thompson, Sld	220	T3Cy.	78	-	
1886 Santiago	93098	4154G Raylton Dixon, Mbro	-	T3Cy.	400	-	
1886 Heraclides	93689	2977G Boold, Sld	19	T3Cy.	450	-	LR(04) 319NHP

YEAR SHIP	OFFNO	TONNA BUILDER	YARD	TYPE	NHP	IHP	REMARKS
1886 Euterpe	Austria	2270G J.L.Thompson, Sld	218	T3Cy.	330	-	
1886 Lusitania	65888	3877G Laird Bros, B'head	381	T3Cy.	638	-	Built 1871:Tripled & NB TR '86
1886 Moyune	91986	2690G J.L.Thompson, Sld	221	T3Cy.	434	-	
1886 Talavera	92852	1628G J.L.Thompson, Sld	216	T3Cy.	150	-	
1886 Spartan	82421	3403G J & G Thomson, Ggow	182	T3Cy.	614	-	Blt. 1881. Tripled 1886 TR.
1886 Rembrandt	90335	1828G J.L.Thompson, Sld	217	T3Cy.	160	-	
1886 Athenian	82425	3782G Aitken, Mansell,Ggw	110	T3Cy.	600	-	Blt.'81: tripled by TR '86
1886 Hubbuck	91912	2749G J.L.Thompson, Sld	211	T3Cy.	400	-	LR 319 NHP
1886 African / Graceful	92034	1372G Raylton Dixon, Mbro	266	T3Cy.	200	-	
1886 Swiftsure	79632	- Raylton Dixon, Mbr	--	T3Cy.	180	-	Blt. 1878: NE or Conv. '86
1887 Drummond Castle	82861	3705G J. Elder, Glasgow	-	T 3Cy	500	3700	Blt.'81:tripled TR '87(Conv)
1887 Trojan	82404	3471G J & G Thomson G'gow	177	T 3Cy	614	4300	Blt.'80: conversion by TR
1887 Murrumbidgee/Peninsul.	94330	2744G J.L.Thompson, Sld	228	T3Cy.	400	2100	
1887 Wave / Antonios	92912	2264G Wm. Gray, W.H'pl	320	T3Cy.	200	1200	
1887 Vulcan	92910	2205G E. Withy, Hpl	143	T3Cy.	190	1200	
1887 Mexican	86330	4549G J. Laing, Sld	273	T3Cy.	600	3370	Blt. '82.Tripled TR 1887(Conv)
1887 Foyle	94325	2454G J.L.Thompson, Sld	215	T3Cy.	300	1600	
1887 Rubens	94315	2153G J.L.Thompson, Sld	223	T3Cy.	250	1250	
1887 Rockcliff	92913	2288G E. Withy, Hpl	144	T3Cy.	180	1200	
1887 Beneficent	84996	1978G Short Bros, Sld	120	C2Cy.	180	-	Built 1881. NE TR 1887.
1887 Grantully Castle	81601	3489G Barclay, Curle G'gw	290	T 3Cy	550	2430	Blt. 1879: tripled TR 1887
1887 Royal Jubilee	--	J.L.Thompson, Sld	221	? T3Cy.		-	Possibly name soon changed.
1887 Tartar / Kokura Maru	91000	2389G Raylton Dixon, Mbro	250	T3Cy.	400	1900	
1887 Moor / La Plata	82428	3597G J.G.Thomson, G'gow	184	T3Cy.	810	4700	Blt. 1881. Tripled & NB TR '87
1887 Melbourne	98524	1739G Edw. Withy, Hpl	-	T3Cy.	180	1200	
1887 Haitan	88844	1856G Raylton Dixon, Mbro	272	T3Cy.	350	1600	
1887 Roddam	94327	2365G E. Withy, Hpl	147	T3Cy.	200	1250	
1887 Thomsonian/R.Harrowing	89782	2069G J.L.Thompson, Sld	207	T3Cy.	240	1400	LR(00) 225NHP
1888 Oswestry	92928	2366G E. Withy, Hpl	153	T3Cy.	250	-	
1888 Roslin Castle	87126	4267G Barclay Curle, G'gw	316	T 3Cy	800	-	Blt.'83. Conversion by TR.
1888 Echuca / Catania	95520	2826G Raylton Dixon, Mbro	289	T3Cy.	400	-	
1888 Resolution	89788	1979G J.L.Thompson, Sld	235	T3Cy.	181	-	
1888 Garth Castle /Ismailia	82849	3705G J. Elder, Glasgow	245	T 3Cy	600	-	Blt 1880:conv. to T3Cy by TR
1888 Pallion	78424	1723G Wm. Gray, W.H'pl	199	C2Cy.	150	-	Blt.1879 . New Boilers only.
1888 Nam Yong ex J.B.Walker	70432	1512G Raylton Dixon, Mbro	114	T3Cy.	150 ·	-	Blt 1875 Tripled TR 1888.
1888 Sapphire	94392	2058G Richdsn Duck, Stktn	352	T3Cy.	200	-	
1888 Discovery	89790	1916G J.L.Thompson, Sld	236	T3Cy.	180	-	
1888 Arbib Brothers	95517	2653G Swan Hunter N/C	136	T3Cy.	230	-	
1888 Eugenie	Norway	2335G Raylton Dixon, Mbro	-	T3Cy.	190	-	
1888 Ursa	95880	2735G E. Withy, Hpl	157	T3Cy.	260	-	
1888 Nith	94393	2284G E. Withy, Hpl	152	T3Cy.	217	-	
1888 Guy Colin / Aquila	94390	2234G Raylton Dixon, Mbro	284	T3Cy.	250	-	
1888 Hawkhurst	95478	2340G Richdsn Duck, Stktn	356	T3Cy.	200	-	
1888 Enterprize	95661	2002G J.L.Thompson, Sld	237	T3Cy.	180	-	
1888 Longstone	95474	2309G Raylton Dixon, Mbro	-	T3Cy.	200	-	LR 220 NHP
1888 Juno	95877	2430G E. Withy, Hpl	155	T3Cy.	232	-	
1888 Age	88959	2216G E. Withy, Hpl	151	T3Cy.	217	-	
1888 Nigretia	93802	2368G Raylton Dixon, Mbro	286	T3Cy.	217	-	
1888 Chicklade	95884	2374G E. Withy, Hpl	158	T3Cy.	200	-	
1888 Tartar	86336	4435G Aitken, Mansell,Ggw	116	T3Cy.	684	-	Blt.1883.Tripled TR 1888(Conv
1889 Ebro	95800	2414G Richdsn Duck, Stktn	362	T3Cy.	200	1300	
1889 Rotherfield	96659	2831G E. Withy, Hpl	165	T3Cy.	300	1600	
1889 Scots Greys	70700	1823G Raylton Dixon, Mbro	-	T3Cy.	180	1000	Blt.'75. Tripled by TR '89

YEAR	SHIP	OFFNO	TONNA	BUILDER	YARD	TYPE	NHP	IHP	REMARKS
1889	Palentino / Palestro	109437	2354G	R. Thompson, Sld	158	T3Cy.	308	1850	
1889	Ethiope / Polyxeni	96303	2893G	Raylton Dixon, Mbro	295	T3Cy.	250	1600	LR(00) 265NHP
1889	Moonstone	96577	2140G	Richdsn Duck, Stktn	359	T3Cy.	200	1150	
1889	Hudson / Anglia	78419	1630G	Wm. Gray, W.H'pl	193	T3Cy.	214	1650	built 1878: re-engined Tr '89
1889	Hibernia	96544	2418G	Raylton Dixon, Mbro	303	T3Cy.	210	1500	
1889	Douro	95796	2383G	Richdsn Duck, Stktn	361	T3Cy.	200	1300	
1889	Daylight	97365	2338G	Raylton Dixon, Mbro	-	T3Cy.	200	1250	
1889	Khio	95288	2376G	E. Withy, Hpl	160	T3Cy.	220	1300	LR 232 NHP
1889	Jordan	95533	2071G	J.L.Thompson, Sld	249	T3Cy.	250	-	
1889	Daventry	95899	2837G	E. Withy, Hpl	161	T3Cy.	217	1250	
1889	Inchmarlo / Allendale	96357	3057G	R. Thompson, Sld	156	T3Cy.	-	1850	
1889	Ovingdean Grange	98051	2413G	Raylton Dixon, Mbro	308	T3Cy.	400	2250	
1889	Kennett	95525	1707G	E. Withy, Hpl	162	T3Cy.	170	-	
1889	G.R.Booth	95298	2454G	Raylton Dixon, Mbro	299	T3Cy.	250	-	
1889	Verax	97382	2531G	E. Withy, Hpl	167	T3Cy.	180	1250	
1889	Alhena / Norrland	93879	2279G	Raylton Dixon, Mbro	294	T3Cy.	220	-	
1889	Apache	n.k.		Raylton Dixon, Mbro	-	T3Cy.	-	-	
1889	Dalmally	97364	2472G	E. Withy, Hpl	164	T3Cy.	180	1250	
1889	Urbino	95787	2351G	R. Thompson, Sld	153	T3Cy.	217	-	
1889	City of Belfast	96251	2226G	Short Bros, Sld	188	T3Cy.	180	1150	
1889	Florence	95296	2492G	Short Bros, Sld	189	T3Cy.	200	1250	
1889	Glenartney	97588	3026G	J. Laing, Sld	332	T3Cy.	400	2550	
1889	Leif Eriksson	Norway	2182G	Laxevaags, Bergen	28	T3Cy.	201	-	2910 DWT
1889	Tunbridge	n.k.	2356G	Raylton Dixon, Mbro	-	T3Cy.	225	1250	
1889	Magnus Mail	95287	2251G	Short Bros, Sld	184	T3Cy.	202	1150	
1889	Matatua	96168	3322G	R. Stephenson N/C	15	T3Cy.	329	2050	
1889	Sheerness / Mouro	95788	2131G	Richdsn Duck, Stktn	366	T3Cy.	203	1150	
1889	Wastwater	95891	2874G	E. Withy, Hpl	159	T3Cy.	265	1600	
1889	Staffa	97370	2080G	E. Withy, Hpl	166	T3Cy.	220	1250	
1889	Elba	96590	2293G	Raylton Dixon, Mbro	-	T3Cy.	300	1500	
1890	Vesuvio ex Kate Fawcet	Italy	1388G	E. Withy, Hpl	52	T3Cy.	163	-	Blt 1876. Tripled TR 1890.
1890	Blenheim	98043	2248G	E. Withy, Hpl	169	T3Cy.	200	-	
1890	Reijniersz	Holland	644 G	Mj. De Maas, R'dam	-	T3Cy.	116	-	Contract to fitted 11 weeks.
1890	Paranagua	France	1988G	Raylton Dixon, Mbro	310	T3Cy.	325	-	LR(00) 241NHP
1890	Capenor	98162	2536G	E. Withy, Hpl	175	T3Cy.	210	-	
1890	Norse King	98071	2985G	J. Laing, Sld	333	T3Cy.	450	-	
1890	Alacrity	96557	2190G	E. Withy, Hpl	176	T3Cy.	190	-	
1890	Robert Eggleton	97523	2308G	Short Bros, Sld	186	T3Cy.	196	-	
1890	Culgoa	96681	3325G	J.L.Thompson, Sld	257	T3Cy.	450	2750	
1890	Bona	98052	2427G	Raylton Dixon, Mbro	311	T3Cy.	250	-	
1890	Prins Willem I	Holland	1677G	Richdsn Duck, Stktn	376	T3Cy.	240	-	
1890	George Allen	97527	2309G	Short Bros, Sld	196	T3Cy.	200	-	
1890	Hesper	98492	2720G	Ropner, Stockton	252	T3Cy.	221	-	
1890	Storm King	98094	3279G	Raylton Dixon, Mbro	304	T3Cy.	419	-	
1890	Ruskin	98101	2392G	Raylton Dixon, Mbro	314	T3Cy.	225	-	
1890	Ashlands	97398	2303G	E. Withy, Hpl	173	T3Cy.	200	-	
1890	Zampa	97394	2364G	E. Withy, Hpl	171	T3Cy.	200	-	
1890	Vala	98890	2536G	Richdsn Duck, Stktn	383	T3Cy.	200	-	LR 217 NHP
1890	Monrovia	97775	2402G	Raylton Dixon, Mbro	313	T3Cy.	190	-	
1890	Baria / Kambyses	Germany	3020G	J. Laing, Sld	338	T3Cy.	304	-	vide "The Engineer" 31.10.90
1890	Beatrice	95326	657 G	Richdsn Duck, Stktn	368	T3Cy.	99	750	
1890	Mayumba	97821	2516G	Raylton Dixon, Mbro	329	T3Cy.	232	-	
1891	Dunmurry	96273	2592G	Short Bros, Sld	202	T3Cy.	250	-	Lost 1891.

THOS. RICHARDSON MARINE ENGINES: 1851-1900

YEAR	SHIP	OFFNO	TONNA	BUILDER	YARD	TYPE	NHP	IHP	REMARKS
1891	Sydenham	98963	2377G	E. Withy, Hpl	183	T3Cy.	217	-	
1891	Oil Rivers / Cabenda	97845	2500G	Raylton Dixon, Mbro	330	T3Cy.	258	-	
1891	Aden	98775	3925G	Raylton Dixon, Mbro	340	T3Cy.	471	-	
1891	Norton	98521	2395G	Irvine & Co., W.Hpl	74	T3Cy.	165	-	LR(95) 221 NHP
1891	Dictator	97890	4116G	Raylton Dixon, Mbro	335	T3Cy.	400	-	
1891	Angola	97875	2870G	Raylton Dixon, Mbro	332	T3Cy.	257	-	
1891	Aymestry	98508	3049G	Ropner, Stockton	258	T3Cy.	250	-	
1891	Phyllis	98511	2429G	Ropner, Stockton	259	T3Cy.	240	-	
1891	Salopia	98951	2404G	E. Withy, Hpl	182	T3Cy.	200	-	
1891	Wildcroft	98905	2958G	E. Withy, Hpl	179	T3Cy.	300	-	
1891	Welldeck/Inchdune	97877	2697G	Irvine & Co., W.Hpl	71	T3Cy.	298	-	
1891	Velleda	98929	2545G	Richdsn Duck, Stktn	384	T3Cy.	221	-	
1891	Avona	98906	2889G	Richdsn Duck, Stktn	378	T3Cy.	232	-	
1891	Zanni Stefanovich	n.k.	2333G	E. Withy, Hpl	186	T3Cy.	200	-	
1891	Chatfield	98896	2931G	Irvine & Co., W.Hpl	70	T3Cy.	200	-	
1891	Glenisle / Villalegre	98499	1847G	E. Withy, Hpl	177	T3Cy.	180	-	LR 168 NHP
1891	Emma	98518	2893G	Irvine & Co., W.Hpl	73	T3Cy.	180	-	
1891	Drot	Norway	2274G	Laxevaags, Bergen	34	T3Cy.	245	-	4125 DWT
1891	Castleventry	98509	2994G	E. Withy, Hpl	181	T3Cy.	275	-	
1891	Nutfield	98944	2566G	Richdsn Duck, Stktn	386	T3Cy.	200	-	
1891	Atlantic	97546	2478G	Raylton Dixon, Mbro	352	T3Cy.	221	-	
1891	Huntcliff	98516	3120G	Ropner, Stockton	261	T3Cy.	175	-	
1891	Wooler	98969	2403G	E. Withy, Hpl	184	T3Cy.	200	-	LR(95) 221NHP
1891	Pembridge	98922	2935G	Raylton Dixon, Mbro	-	T3Cy.	240	-	
1891	Dahomey	98996	2854G	Raylton Dixon, Mbro	339	T3Cy.	240	-	
1891	Pindari	99338	5713G	Harland & Wolff Bst	245	T3Cy.	429	-	Twin Screw.
1891	Kintuck	98923	3596G	Raylton Dixon, Mbro	326	T3Cy.	750	-	LR 483 NHP
1891	Melbridge/Calcutta C.	98505	2868G	E. Withy, Hpl	180	T3Cy.	300	-	LR 270 NHP
1892	Albion	98522	3650G	Ropner, Stockton	268	T3Cy.	250	-	
1892	Falkland / Georgios	99808	2918G	Tyne Iron S.B. N/C	92	T3Cy.	250	-	
1892	Teutonia	Holland	3209G	Ropner, Stockton	269	T3Cy.	266	-	
1892	Stranton	81508	1754G	Wm. Gray, W.H'pl	213	T3Cy.	187	-	Blt. 1880 with TR Compound 2Cy
1892	Afrikander	99047	2755G	Raylton Dixon, Mbro	361	T3Cy.	283	-	
1892	Pendarves	99156	2669G	Raylton Dixon, Mbro	366	T3Cy.	250	-	LR 244 NHP
1892	Kaffir	99062	2736G	Raylton Dixon, Mbro	360	T3Cy.	500	-	LR 283 NHP
1892	Baron Ardrossan	97563	2823G	Raylton Dixon, Mbro	358	T3Cy.	249	-	
1892	Lobelia	98533	2942G	Irvine & Co., W.Hpl	77	T3Cy.	180	-	LR 249 NHP
1892	Starlight	98527	2946G	Irvine & Co., W.Hpl	75	T3Cy.	165	-	
1892	Pallion	78424	1293G	Wm. Gray, W.H'pl	199	T3Cy.	187	-	Blt. 1879: Tripled TR 1892
1892	Eastry	98526	3015G	Furness Withy, Hpl	190	T3Cy.	259	-	
1892	Horsley Tower /Horatio	101913	3212G	Edwards S/B Co. N/C	60	T3Cy.	287	-	
1892	Great Northern	63584	1316G	Denton, Gray Hpl	91	T3Cy.	145	-	Blt. 1870: New E & B TR 1892
1892	Cardinal	101816	2303G	Furness Withy, Hpl	194	T3Cy.	201	-	
1892	Transvaal	101895	2746G	Raylton Dixon, Mbro	362	T3Cy.	283	-	
1892	Straits of Dover	99842	2931G	Irvine & Co., W.Hpl	76	T3Cy.	180	-	
1892	Zulu	99056	2746G	Raylton Dixon, Mbro	363	T3Cy.	283	-	
1892	Topaze	79664	1902G	C. Swan, Hunter,N/C	39	T3Cy.	187	-	Blt 1878. Tripled TR 1892
1892	Birdoswald/Glanystwyth	98000	2993G	Furness Withy, Hpl	191	T3Cy.	266	-	
1892	Glenwood	98531	1712G	Furness Withy, Hpl	193	T3Cy.	168	-	
1892	Powderham	99264	3019G	Raylton Dixon, Mbro	367	T3Cy.	266	-	
1893	Phoenix / Cairndon	101993	2692G	Raylton Dixon, Mbro	382	T3Cy.	266	-	
1893	Empress	98536	2918G	Furness Withy, Hpl	196	T3Cy.	249	-	
1893	Zaire	Belgium	3156G	Raylton Dixon, Mbro	388	T3Cy.	413	-	

YEAR	SHIP	OFFNO	TONNA	BUILDER	YARD	TYPE	NHP	IHP	REMARKS
1893	Sirona / Horda	102796	2927G	Richdsn Duck, Stktn	407	T3Cy.	250	-	
1893	Chiltern	56155	1297G	Denny, Dumbarton	-	T3Cy.	250	-	Blt.1866. New E TR '93. Cable.
1893	Barrister	102077	4750G	Raylton Dixon, Mbro	369	T 3Cy	500	-	
1893	Stolzenfels	Germany	3022G	Raylton Dixon, Mbro	368	T3Cy.	273	-	
1893	Orpington	87032	2284G	J.L.Thompson, Sld	-	T3Cy.	217	-	Blt. 1882: New E & B TR 1893
1893	Greenbrier	102707	2875G	Furness Withy, Hpl	201	T 3Cy	412	-	
1893	Rothenfels	Germany	2935G	Raylton Dixon, Mbro	395	T3Cy.	249	-	
1893	Cayo Mono	102807	2711G	Swan Hunter N/C	189	T3Cy.	267	-	
1893	Beltisloe	99692	2869G	Furness Withy, Hpl	198	T 3Cy	262	-	
1893	Sybil	81562	1945G	J.L.Thompson, Sld	149	T3Cy.	183	-	Blt. 1879: New E & B TR '93
1893	Appomattox	102704	2875G	Furness Withy, Hpl	199	T3Cy.	412	-	
1894	Prins Willem IV	Holland	1724G	Richdsn Duck, Stktn	428	T3Cy.	240	-	
1894	Saint Jerome	102166	2949G	Furness Withy, Hpl	207	T3Cy.	240	-	
1894	Leyden / Benedict	106827	3378G	Raylton Dixon, Mbro	399	T3Cy.	334	-	
1894	Phoebe	98449	2754G	Turnbull, Whitby	126	T3Cy.	240	-	
1894	Florence	83669	2128G	Turnbull, Whitby	71	T3Cy.	220	-	Blt. 1881. New E & B TR 1894
1894	Cundall	102721	2416G	Furness Withy, Hpl	208	T3Cy.	221	-	
1894	Ceylon / Yamato Maru	98785	4094G	Raylton Dixon, Mbro	355	T3Cy.	470	-	
1894	Manningtry	102715	2845G	Furness Withy, Hpl	204	T3Cy.	253	-	
1894	Atala	104848	3250G	Richdsn Duck, Stktn	444	T3Cy.	267	-	
1894	Lindenfels / Ghazipur	Germany	2932G	Raylton Dixon, Mbro	396	T3Cy.	273	-	
1894	Maristow / Enecuri	102437	2385G	Raylton Dixon, Mbro	400	T3Cy.	224	-	
1894	George Pyman	102714	2055G	Irvine & Co., W.Hpl	90	T3Cy.	193	-	
1894	Horsa	102709	2949	Wm. Gray, West H'pl	470	T3Cy.	256	-	Eng.No.from Gray's Yard Book.
1894	Dovedale	99723	2821G	Ropner, Stockton	297	T3Cy.	249	-	
1895	Steinberger	Germany	3583G	Raylton Dixon, Mbro	407	T3Cy.	316	-	
1895	Ibex	104847	2397G	Irvine & Co., W.Hpl	93	T3Cy.	217	-	
1895	Leopoldville / Biafra	Belgium	2739G	Raylton Dixon, Mbro	402	T3Cy.	308	-	
1895	Michelangelo	Italy	2498G	J.Laing, Sld	537	T3Cy.	260	-	LR(04) 228NHP
1895	Benridge / Ontanda	105285	3448G	Craig Taylor, Stktn	42	T3Cy.	262	-	
1895	Lady Furness	105716	3158G	Furness Withy, Hpl	216	T3Cy.	299	-	
1895	Ailsawald	104274	2921G	Furness Withy, Hpl	210	T3Cy.	240	-	
1895	Thracia	Germany		Raylton Dixon, Mbro	-	T3Cy.	258	-	10 knots. THIS VSL DOUBTFUL.
1895	Ockenfels	Germany	3589G	Raylton Dixon, Mbro	410	T3Cy.	315	-	
1895	Ras Elba	105760	2735G	Furness Withy, Hpl	218	T3Cy.	240	-	
1895	Nordhvalen	Denmark	3112G	Richdsn Duck	449	T3Cy.	267	-	
1895	Benrath / Oleta	105281	3448G	Craig Taylor, Stktn	41	T3Cy.	262	-	
1895	Mobile	102737	3341G	Furness Withy, Hpl	219	T3Cy.	292	-	
1895	Vasco	105060	1914G	Furness Withy, Hpl	217	T3Cy.	188	-	
1895	Rauma	Norway	3048G	Raylton Dixon, Mbro	411	T3Cy.	268	-	
1895	Verbena	102728	2364G	Furness Withy, Hpl	213	T3Cy.	224	-	
1896	Reindeer	105848	2412G	J.Priestman, Sld	60	T3Cy.	217	-	
1896	Albertville / Jebba	Belgium	3812G	Raylton Dixon, Mbro	421	T3Cy.	419	-	n/a
1896	Leonis / Skyros	106951	2611G	Furness Withy, Hpl	225	T3Cy.	226	-	
1896	Taquary	Germany	2788G	Raylton Dixon, Mbro	423	T3Cy.	218	-	Blt. 1887 ? New Engine TR ?
1896	Sardonyx	105856	2794G	Raylton Dixon, Mbro	422	T3Cy.	244	-	
1896	Montgomery	106953	3471G	W. Doxford, Sld	245	T3Cy.	292	-	Doxford turret ship.
1896	Selma	102745	3480G	W. Doxford, Sld	240	T3Cy.	292	-	Turret Deck.
1896	Wolfsburg	Germany	2489G	Raylton Dixon, Mbro	418	T3Cy.	274	-	
1896	Lincluden	102743	2746G	Furness Withy, Hpl	221	T3Cy.	265	-	
1896	Rudelsburg	German	2334G	Raylton Dixon, Mbro	417	T3Cy.	249	-	
1896	Huron	105884	3090G	J.L.Thompson, Sld	344	T3Cy.	271	-	
1896	Maceio	Germany	2400G	Raylton Dixon, Mbro	424	T3Cy.	218	-	

THOS. RICHARDSON MARINE ENGINES: 1851-1900

YEAR	SHIP	OFFNO	TONNA	BUILDER	YARD	TYPE	NHP	IHP	REMARKS
1896	Suningdale	106954	2584G	Ropner, Stockton	328	T3Cy.	225	-	
1896	Dorothy	102746	2445G	Ropner, Stockton	319	T3Cy.	224	-	
1897	Tai Hoko	Japan	3179G	Raylton Dixon, Mbr	439 ?	T3Cy	552	-	
1897	Apollo	106610	4062G	Furness Withy, Hpl	228	T3Cy.	294	-	
1897	Min	108262	3083G	J.L.Thompson, Sld	353	T3Cy.	270	-	
1897	Verona	106060	3463G	Short Bros, Sld	263	T3Cy.	328	-	LR(00) 292NHP
1897	Scottish King /Aboukir	108151	3317G	Short Bros, Sld	260	T3Cy.	450	-	LR(04) gives HP Cyl 37"
1897	Venetia	108701	3596G	Short Bros, Sld	265	T3Cy.	328	-	LR(00) 292NHP
1897	Montrose	108251	5440G	Raylton Dixon, Mbro	441	T3Cy.	632	-	
1897	Leopoldville / Sekondi	Belgium	3760G	Raylton Dixon, Mbro	430	T3Cy.	419	-	
1898	Albertville	Belgium	3805G	Raylton Dixon, Mbro	449	T3Cy.	432	-	
1898	Albanian	110523	2930G	R.Thompson, Sld	205	T3Cy.	288	-	
1898	Gambia / Vega	109414	2877G	Raylton Dixon, Mbro	448	T3Cy.	253	-	
1898	Meridian	99500	3488G	W. Doxford, Sld	260	T3Cy.	292	-	Turret deck.
1898	Bruxellesville	Belgium	3757G	Raylton Dixon, Mbro	447	T3Cy.	432	-	
1898	Ashton	108372	3196G	J.L.Thompson, Sld	361	T3Cy.	280	-	
1898	Maylands	106292	2517G	Furness Withy, Hpl	233	T3Cy.	232	-	
1898	Winifred	106987	2794G	Irvines S/bldg	104	T3Cy.	267	-	
1898	Heathdene	106644	3542G	Hawthorn Leslie,N/C	364	T3Cy.	292	-	
1898	Reynolds	108340	3264G	J.L.Thompson, Sld	359	T3Cy.	271	-	
1898	Dart	108395	3207G	J.L.Thompson, Sld	363	T3Cy.	286	-	
1898	Laura	106980	2715G	Irvines S/bldg	103	T3Cy.	267	-	
1898	Victoria / Manitou	106971	6849G	Furness Withy, Hpl	231	T3Cy.	763	-	
1898	Orono	109921	2891G	Raylton Dixon, Mbro	459	T3Cy.	258	-	
1898	Severn	109235	3760G	Raylton Dixon, Mbro	453	T3Cy.	542	-	
1898	Assyrian	109403	2890G	Furness Withy, Hpl	234	T3Cy.	288	-	
1899	Anna	Austria	2033G	Craig Taylor, Stktn	61	T3Cy.	222	-	
1899	North Sea	110181	1711G	Craig Taylor, Stktn	64	T3Cy.	265	-	
1899	Nordpol	Norway	3715G	North'b'ld S/B N/C	77	T3Cy.	304	-	
1899	Giuseppe Accame	Italy	3077G	Hofer Manaira,Spez.	1	T3Cy.	228	-	
1899	Etruria	Germany	1659G	Craig Taylor, Stktn	65	T3Cy.	225	-	
1899	Ferndene	110342	3752G	North'b'ld S/B,N/C	78	T3Cy.	316	-	
1899	Saxon Prince	110336	3471G	Short Bros, Sld	282	T3Cy.	312	-	
1899	Portugal	n.k.	3897G	Raylton Dixon, Mbro	464	T3Cy.	504	-	
1899	Kum Sang	110076	3237G	Raylton Dixon, Mbro	461	T3Cy.	370	-	
1899	Milton	110120	3267G	J.L.Thompson, Sld	371	T3Cy.	265	-	
1899	Hatasu	110103	3358G	Furness Withy, Hpl	241	T3Cy.	284	-	
1899	Clumberhall	112410	3599G	Irvines S/bldg	109	T3Cy.	289	-	PROBABLY RW (H'pool)
1899	Lucifer	110609	3823G	Swan Hunter, Nwc	246	T3Cy.	310	-	Engines aft. Oil Tanker.
1899	Antonietta Accame	Italy	3831G	Muggiano, Italy	3	T3Cy.	228	-	
1899	Robert Irvine	112402	3583G	Irvines S/bldg	108	T3Cy.	297	-	
1899	Romney	110532	4464G	Raylton Dixon, Mbro	456	T3Cy.	390	-	
1899	Claverdale	110069	3307G	Craig Taylor, Stktn	58	T3Cy.	278	-	
1899	Achanda	Spain	2058G	Craig Taylor, Stktn	62	T3Cy.	222	-	
1899	Degama	110557	3507G	Furness Withy, Hpl	240	T3Cy.	271	-	
1899	Granada	Germany	4842G	J.Priestman, Sld	80	T3Cy.	436	-	PROBABLY RW (H'pool)
1899	Palatinia	108837	3620G	Furness Withy, Hpl	239	T3Cy.	292	-	
1899	Ravenshoe	109782	3592G	North'b'ld S/B N/C	76	T3Cy.	301	-	
1900	Cerea	Italy	4295G	Muggiano, La Spezia	7	T3Cy.	356	-	PROBABLY RW (H'pool)
1900	Ismailia	111276	4984G	Raylton Dixon, Mbro	469	T3Cy.	405	-	
1900	Proteo	Aust-Hung	3813G	Swan Hunter, N/C	256	T3Cy.	310	-	PROBABLY RW (H'pool)
1900	Corso	113530	1778G	Raylton Dixon, Mbro	472	T3Cy.	190	-	LR states TR.
1900	Hartburn	110356	2184G	Blyth S/B Co. Blyth	102	T3Cy.	257	-	PROBABLY RW (H'pool)

THOS. RICHARDSON MARINE ENGINES: 1851-1900

YEAR	SHIP	OFFNO	TONNA	BUILDER	YARD	TYPE	NHP	IHP	REMARKS
1900	Dacia	Germany	3470G	Swan, Hunter N/C	248	T3Cy.	311	-	
1900	Belgian	113417	3740G	J. Laing, Sld	579	T3Cy.	366	-	11 knots. PROBABLY RW (H'pool)
1900	Whangape	110641	2931G	Raylton Dixon, Mbro	470	T3Cy.	255	-	
1900	Sevilla	Germany	5172G	J.Priestman, Sld	81	T3Cy.	436	-	PROBABLY RW (H'pool)
1900	Manica / Huntball	112782	4118G	J. Laing, Sld	580	T3Cy.	530	-	PROBABLY RW (H'pool).
1900	Nina	Spain.	3574G	Craig Taylor, Stktn	73	T3Cy.	278	-	PROBABLY RW (H'pool)
1900	Ruth	Norway	3449G	Swan Hunter, Nwc	250	T3Cy.	275	-	PROBABLY RW (H'pool).
1900	Islanda	111246	5237G	Raylton Dixon, Mbro	468	T3Cy.	405	-	
1900	Woodburn	110365	2360G	Blyth S/B Co. Blyth	103	T3Cy.	257	1000	PROBABLY RW (H'pool).
1900	Kobe	n.k.	4569G	Craig Taylor, Stktn	75	T3Cy.	168	1500	PROBABLY RW (H'pool).
1900	Macedonia	112699	1650G	Craig Taylor, Stktn	66	T3Cy.	225	-	
1900	Runo	109705	4016G	J. Laing, Sld	572	T3Cy.	464		
1900	Consuelo	110797	6025G	Swan Hunter N/C	251	T6Cy.	711	-	Twin screw. PROBABLY RW (H'pl)
1900	Bergedorf	Germany	5270G	Raylton Dixon, Mbro	471	T3Cy.	534	-	PROBABLY RW (H'pool).

YEAR	SHIP	OFFNO	TONNAGE	BUILDER	YARDNO	TYPE	ENGNO	IHP	SHP	REMARKS
899	Clumberhall	112410	3599	Irvines S/B, W. Hpl	109	T3Cy.	1086	1250	-	
899	Granada	Germany	5124	Priestman & Co. Sld	80	T3Cy.	1089	2350	-	
900	Ruth	Norway	3449	Swan, Hunter Nwc	250	T3Cy.	1087	1200	-	
900	Bergedorf	Germany	5270	Raylton Dixon, Mbro	471	T3Cy.	1097	3050	-	
900	Nina	Aust/Hung.	3574	Craig Taylor, Stktn	73	T3Cy.	1096	1035	-	
900	Proteo	Aust/Hung.	3813	Swan, Hunter Nwc	256	T3Cy.	1103	1250	-	
900	Corso	113530	1778	Raylton Dixon, Mbro	472	T3Cy.	1098	700	-	
900	Belgian	113417	3657	J. Laing, Sld	579	T3Cy.	1088	2400	-	
900	Sevilla	Germany	5135	Priestman & Co. Sld	81	T3Cy.	1090	2000	-	
900	Cerea	Italy	4469	Cant.Muggiano,Spezia	7	T3Cy.	1091	1600	-	
900	Consuelo	110797	6025	Swan, Hunter Nwc	251	T3Cy.	1093	4800	-	Twin screw.
900	Manica	112782	4118	J. Laing, Sld	580	T3Cy.	1099	2500	-	
900	Woodburn	110365	2360	Blyth S/B Co., Blyth	103	T3Cy.	1102	1000	-	
900	Hartburn	110356	2367	Blyth S/B Co., Blyth	102	T3Cy.	1101	1000	-	
901	Lustleigh	111359	3250	Craggs, Middlesbro'	167	T3Cy.	1114	1200	-	
901	Thistledhu	114638	4026	Irvines S/B, W. Hpl	122	T3Cy.	1125	1300	-	
901	Kobe	Aust/Hung.	4569	Craig Taylor, Stktn	75	T3Cy.	1107	1500	-	
901	York Castle	112489	5310	J. Laing, Sld	582	T3Cy.	1109			
901	Lake Manitoba	113497	9674	Swan, Hunter, Nwc	263	T3Cy.	1115	4000	-	Twin screw.
901	Epirus	Greece	3276	Craggs & Sons, Mbro	166	T3Cy.	1108	1100	-	
901	Austriana	112448	4025	Irvines S/B, W. Hpl	120	T3Cy.	1117	1300	-	
901	Parthenia	113949	5160	Furness Withy, Hpl	254	T3Cy.	1112	2500	-	
901	Dora Baltea	Italy	4243	Cant.Muggiano,Spezia	10	T3Cy.	1094	1150	-	
901	Thespis	115237	4343	Raylton Dixon, Mbro	484	T3Cy.	1131	3000	-	
901	Horsley	112447	3717	W. Doxford, Sld	290	T3Cy.	1111	1250	-	
901	Soesdyk	Holland	6445	Furness Withy, Hpl	255	T3Cy.	1113	2500	-	
901	Edale	113902	3110	Craggs, Middlesbro'	171	T3Cy.	1128	1150	-	
901	Fert	Italy	4218	Cant.Muggiano,Spezia	11	T3Cy.	1095	1600	-	
901	Nigeria	114747	3755	Raylton Dixon, Mbro	479	T3Cy.	1119	2100	-	
901	Birmingham	115123	4027	Irvines S/B, W. Hpl	121	T3Cy.	1118	1300	-	
901	Amsteldyk	Holland	6435	Furness Withy, Hpl	256	T3Cy.	1120	2500	-	
901	Il Piemonto	Italy	6025	Cant.Muggiano,Spezia	9	T3Cy.	1092	2500	-	
901	Manchester Exchange	113113	4091	Furness Withy, Hpl	257	T3Cy.	1122	1750	-	
901	Barotse	112825	4119	J. Laing, Sld	581	T3Cy.	1100	2500	-	
901	Corneille	France	1900	Raylton Dixon, Mbro	473	T3Cy.	1110	700	-	
901	Barendrecht	Holland	3223	Craggs, Middlesbro'	170	T3Cy.	1127	1150	-	
902	Grovehurst	Sweden	1339	Irvines S/B, W. Hpl	129	T3Cy.	1142	660	-	
902	Ramsay	115831	4318	J.L.Thompson, Sld	398	T3Cy.	1130	1300	-	
902	Como	Germany	6464	Furness Withy, Hpl	262	T3Cy.	1134	2600	-	
902	Badenia	Germany	7649	Furness Withy, Hpl	264	T3Cy.	1143	3000	-	
902	Persiana	115139	4032	Irvines S/B, W. Hpl	127	T3Cy.	1140	1300	-	
902	Acacia	115136	2885	Irvines S/B, W. Hpl	126	T3Cy.	1136	1050	-	
902	Principessa Letizia	Italy		Cant.Muggiano,Spezia	16	T3Cy.	1106	1700	-	
902	Grantleyhall	115126	4008	Irvines S/B, W. Hpl	123	T3Cy.	1126	1300	-	
902	Akabo	115268	3814	Raylton Dixon, Mbro	482	T3Cy.	1124	2100	-	
902	Harbart	115799	3310	Craig, Taylor Stktn	84	T3Cy.	1139	1350	-	
902	Sopergo	Italy	4204	Cant.Muggiano,Spezia	14	T3Cy.	1104	1700	-	
902	Foyle	115800	4147	J.L.Thompson, Sld	397	T3Cy.	1129	1300	-	
902	Lake Michigan	115252	9240	Swan, Hunter, Nwc	264	T3Cy.	1116	3400	-	Twin screw.
902	Lena	115850	4146	J.L.Thompson, Sld	399	T3Cy.	1137	1300	-	
902	Azalea	115134	3552	Irvines S/B, W. Hpl	125	T3Cy.	1135	1170	-	
902	Ovid	115901	4159	J.L.Thompson, Sld	402	T3Cy.	1138	1325	-	

MARINE ENGINES BY RICHARDSONS, WESTGARTH (Hartlepool) 1900-1961

YEAR	SHIP	OFFNO	TONNAGE	BUILDER	YARDNO	TYPE	ENGNO	IHP	SHP	REMARKS
1902	Sloterdyk	Holland	6498	Furness Withy, Hpl	260	T3Cy.	1132	2600	-	
1902	Rapallo	Germany	6511	Furness Withy, Hpl	261	T3Cy.	1133	2600	-	
1902	Monviso	Italy	4205	Cant.Muggiano,Spezia	15	T3Cy.	1105	1700	-	
1902	Sirius	Sweden	1375	Irvines S/B, W. Hpl	128	T3Cy.	1141	660	-	
1902	Manchester Market	113115	4091	Furness Withy, Hpl	259	T3Cy.	1123	1750	-	Wrecked 27/4/1903
1903	Inkula	Italy	5137	Cant. Nav. Muggiano	25	T3Cy.	1152	2400	-	
1903	New Oporto	115149	502	Irvines S/B, W. Hpl	132	T3Cy.	1153	810	-	
1903	Oceanic	116149	2218	Irvines S/B, W. Hpl	130	T3Cy.	1150	900	-	
1903	Clan McIntyre	115775	4807	Furness Withy, Hpl	266	T3Cy.	1146	2300	-	
1903	Vera	115161	2972	Irvines S/B, W. Hpl	134	T3Cy.	1156	1150	-	
1903	Sabia	118331	2807	Stephenson, Nwc	81	T3Cy.	1158	1250	-	
1903	Olympic	118579	2217	Irvines S/B, W. Hpl	131	T3Cy.	1151	900	-	
1903	Porpoise	115156	2926	Furness Withy, Hpl	268	T3Cy.	1159	1250	-	
1903	Clan McLeod	115783	4796	Furness Withy, Hpl	267	T3Cy.	1147	2300	-	
1903	Amiral Tronde	France	5589	Atlantique, Ste Naz.	-	T3Cy.	1154	2800	-	CASTINGS ONLY to Ste.Naza
1903	Everton Grange	117831	7274	Furness Withy, Hpl	265	T3Cy.	1144	3000	-	Twin screw.
1903	Bambara	France	2153	Cant. Nav. Muggiano	22	T3Cy.	1148	900	-	
1903	Tjilatjap	Holland	3859	Raylton Dixon, Mbro	497	T3Cy.	1149	1500	-	
1904	Pontop	118646	3024	Furness Withy, Hpl	277	T3Cy.	1186	1250	-	
1904	Magellan	France	6265	Chant. Ste Nazaire	-	T3Cy.	1165	-	-	DRAWINGS ONLY.
1904	Rugbeian	85277	4042	Northb'ld S/B, Nwc	115	T3Cy.	1170	1400	-	
1904	Lincairn	119587	3638	Furness Withy, Hpl	272	T3Cy.	1171	1300	-	
1904	Elixir	115164	2292	Irvines S/B, W. Hpl	135	T3Cy.	1157	1000	-	
1904	Whinfield	118632	2293	Ropner & Co., Stktn	405	T3Cy.	1169	1000	-	
1904	Harcalo	118498	2822	Furness Withy, Hpl	274	T3Cy.	1181	1000	-	
1904	Columba	115383	3912	Stephenson, Nwc	82	T3Cy.	1160	1300	-	
1904	Dagmar	Sweden	3072	Furness Withy, Hpl	275	T3Cy.	1185	1250	-	
1904	Manchester Mariner	119582	4016	Furness Withy, Hpl	270	T3Cy.	1162	1850	-	
1904	Seminole	118637	5864	Furness Withy, Hpl	263	T3Cy.	1145	2400	-	Tanker ex 'Beaumont'
1904	Adriatic	118816	3028	Irvines S/B, W. Hpl	137	T3Cy.	1167	1150	-	
1904	Katherine	115167	2926	Furness Withy, Hpl	273	T3Cy.	1172	1250	-	
1904	Windermere	119548	2292	Irvines S/B, W. Hpl	138	T3Cy.	1168	1000	-	
1904	Waddon	118483	3931	Stephenson, Nwc	83	T3Cy.	1161	1300	-	
1904	Oldhamia	119584	3639	Furness Withy, Hpl	271	T3Cy.	1163	1300	-	
1904	Majestic	118812	3027	Irvines S/B, W. Hpl	136	T3Cy.	1166	1150	-	
1904	Hillbrook	118100	3896	North'ld S/B, Nwc	114	T3Cy.	1164	1550	-	
1904	Claremont	119861	3883	W. Doxford, Sld	326	T3Cy.	1176	1300	-	
1905	Haverstoe	118950	3789	Furness Withy, Hpl	279	T3Cy.	1188	1300	-	
1905	Gloriana	119869	3051	Irvines S/B, W. Hpl	141	T3Cy.	1193	1100	-	
1905	Langoe	122684	3789	Furness Withy, Hpl	280	T3Cy.	1189	1300	-	
1905	Riverina	120729	4758	J. Laing, Sld	610	T3Cy.	1187	4650	-	
1905	Serbury	119882	3873	W. Doxford, Sld	336	T3Cy.	1178	1300	-	
1905	Harmonic	120491	2855	Furness Withy, Hpl	276	T3Cy.	1182	1300	-	
1905	Archbank	118658	3767	Furness Withy, Hpl	281	T3Cy.	1190	1300	-	
1905	Harley	120608	3428	Furness Withy, Hpl	283	T3Cy.	1192	1275	-	1906 'Baron Baeyens'
1905	Apollo	120597	3374	Furness Withy, Hpl	284	T3Cy.	1199	1300	-	
1905	Oswestry	119595	3657	J.L.Thompson, Sld	425	T3Cy.	1210	1325	-	
1905	Orseolo	Italy	4616	Cant.Muggiano,Spezia	27	T3Cy.	1179	1800	-	
1905	Cameron	119881	3044	Irvines S/B, W. Hpl	143	T3Cy.	1194	1100	-	
1905	Harmony	120501	2833	Furness Withy, Hpl	278	T3Cy.	1183	1300	-	
1905	Sandown	119876	3790	Furness Withy, Hpl	282	T3Cy.	1191	1300	-	
1905	Clan McPherson	121274	4779	Furness Withy, Hpl	287	T3Cy.	1205	2300	-	Sunk 4/3/1918
1905	Greenbank	119864	3881	W. Doxford, Sld	328	T3Cy.	1177	1300	-	

MARINE ENGINES BY RICHARDSONS, WESTGARTH (Hartlepool) 1900-1961

AR SHIP	OFFNO	TONNAGE	BUILDER	YARDNO	TYPE	ENGNO	IHP	SHP	REMARKS
)5 Norfolk Range	119218	3098	Irvines S/B, W. Hpl	144	T3Cy.	1195	1100	- -	
)5 Germanic	121011	3477	Irvines S/B, W. Hpl	140	T3Cy.	1184	1300	-	
)5 Pathan	118219	5145	Raylton Dixon, Mbro	517	T3Cy.	1197	2300	-	
)5 Teesbridge	119879	3898	Stephenson, Nwc	90	T3Cy.	1198	1300	-	
)5 Caboto	Italy	4506	Cant.Muggiano,Spezia	28	T3Cy.	1180	1800	-	
)6 Ada	119896	3821	Furness Withy, Hpl	293	T3Cy.	1219	1300	-	
)6 Malvern Range	119224	3594	Furness Withy, Hpl	285	T3Cy.	1201	1275	-	
)6 Corunna	123763	3810	Furness Withy, Hpl	298	T3Cy.	1227	1300	-	
)6 Dipton	122583	3811	Furness Withy, Hpl	293	T3Cy.	1220	1300	-	
)6 Garonne	France		Chant. Ste Nazaire	-	T3Cy.	1211	1300	-	
)6 Elloe	123590	3809	Furness Withy, Hpl	297	T3Cy.	1226	1300	-	
06 Harpenden	123703	3553	Furness Withy, Hpl	295	T3Cy.	1223	1300	-	
)6 Lowther Range	119229	3792	Furness Withy, Hpl	292	T3Cy.	1218	1300	-	
06 Clan McIntosh	121290	4775	Furness Withy, Hpl	288	T3Cy.	1206	2300	-	
)6 Snowdon Range	123942	3060	Irvines S/B, W. Hpl	151	T3Cy.	1202	1100	-	
06 Bessborough	123247	3824	Furness Withy, Hpl	290	T3Cy.	1216	1300	-	
06 Heathpool		3828	Furness Withy, Hpl	291	T3Cy.	1217	1300	-	sunk 10/10/1906
06 Siegmund	Germany	3034	Irvines S/B, W. Hpl	145	T3Cy.	1212	1500	-	
06 Clan Mathieson	121305	4775	Furness Withy, Hpl	289	T3Cy.	1207	2300	-	
06 Gutrune	Germany	3039	Irvines S/B, W. Hpl	148	T3Cy.	1214	1500	-	
06 Coaling	120930	3794	Furness Withy, Hpl	286	T3Cy.	1200	1300	-	ex 'Ikala'
06 Ripon	119900	2965	Irvines S/B, W. Hpl	152	T3Cy.	1204	1175	-	
06 Gunther	Germany	3037	Irvines S/B, W. Hpl	149	T3Cy.	1215	1500	-	
06 Cyclops HMS	Admiralty	--	J. Laing, Sld	609	T3Cy.	1208	4000	-	Twin screw.
06 Linde Fell	124320	3025	Irvines S/B, W. Hpl	154	T3Cy.	1221	1175	-	
06 Sieglinde	Germany	2887	Irvines S/B, W. Hpl	146	T3Cy.	1213	1500	-	
06 Harley	123731	4107	Furness Withy, Hpl	296	T3Cy.	1224	1350	-	
306 Ribston	119895	3048	Irvines S/B, W. Hpl	150	T3Cy.	1203	1100	-	
307 Washington	124342	3031	Irvines S/B, W. Hpl	158	T3Cy.	1233	1200	-	
307 Roanoke	124329	3705	Furness Withy, Hpl	299	T3Cy.	1229	1800	-	
307 Calcutta	125636	3577	Furness Withy, Hpl	305	T3Cy.	1239	1300	-	
307 Mars	125622	3550	Furness Withy, Hpl	304	T3Cy.	1238	1300	-	
307 Competitor	124561	3526	Furness Withy, Hpl	303	T3Cy.	1231	1800	-	
307 Rapidan	124334	3709	Furness Withy, Hpl	300	T3Cy.	1230	1800	-	
307 Newport News	124346	3031	Irvines S/B, W. Hpl	157	T3Cy.	1234	1200	-	
307 Myra Fell	124325	3024	Irvines S/B, W. Hpl	155	T3Cy.	1222	1175	-	
307 Palma	124080	2981	Irvines S/B, W. Hpl	160	T3Cy.	1237	1400	-	
307 Yarra	120737	2257	Furness Withy, Hpl	301	T3Cy.	1232	1100	-	
307			Wiltons, Rotterdam	-	T3Cy.	1240	-	-	CASTINGS ONLY.
307			Wiltons, Rotterdam	-	T3Cy.	1228	-	-	PATTERNS & CASTINGS ONLY.
307 Celebes	Holland	5875	Furness Withy, Hpl	302	T3Cy.	1236	2500	-	
307 Kathleen	123181	3908	Stephenson, Nwc	112	T3Cy.	1235	1350	-	
307 Richmond	124322	2921	Irvines S/B, W. Hpl	156	T3Cy.	1225	1225	-	
308 Arthur	Sweden	1311	Irvines S/B, W. Hpl	167	T3Cy.	1253	675	-	
308 Nora	123193	3926	Stephenson, Nwc	115	T3Cy.	1246	1400	-	
908 Ste. Adresse	France	3056	Chant. Ste Nazaire	-	T3Cy.	1248	1800	-	CASTINGS ONLY.
908 Tuscany	127427	3000	Irvines S/B, W. Hpl	162	T3Cy.	1245	1200	-	
908 Westerwald	Germany	4056	Furness Withy, Hpl	306	T3Cy.	1241	2700	-	
908 Texas	France	6674	Chant. Ste Nazaire	-	T3Cy.	1251	3450	-	CASTINGS ONLY.
308 Frankenwald	Germany	4026	Furness Withy, Hpl	308	T3Cy.	1243	2700	-	
308 Honduras	France	5913	Chant. Ste Nazaire	-	T3Cy.	1250	1800	-	CASTINGS ONLY.
908 Guatemalo	France	5913	Chant. Ste Nazaire	-	T3Cy.	1249	1800	-	CASTINGS ONLY.
908 Gwladys	128484	3929	Stephenson, Nwc	116	T3Cy.	1247	1400	-	

Page 99

YEAR	SHIP	OFFNO	TONNAGE	BUILDER	YARDNO	TYPE	ENGNO	IHP	SHP	REMARKS
1908	Arabiana	127422	3001	Irvines S/B, W. Hpl	161	T3Cy.	1244	1200	-	
1909	Broomhill	125460	1392	Irvines S/B, W. Hpl	169	T3Cy.	1255	725	-	
1909	Werribee	120755	3871	Blyth S/B Co., Blyth	142	T3Cy.	1252	1750	-	
1909	Bassam	128006	3040	Irvines S/B, W. Hpl	313	T3Cy.	1262	1550	-	
1909	Minister Delbeke	Belgium	1832	Irvines S/B, W. Hpl	172	T3Cy.	1263	825	-	
1909	Armistor	129019	2994	Irvines S/B, W. Hpl	310	T3Cy.	1257	1150	-	ex 'Napoliana'
1909	Teessider	124275	1158	Irvines S/B, W. Hpl	168	T3Cy.	1254	2000	-	
1909	Spreewald	Germany	3899	Furness Withy, Hpl	307	T3Cy.	1242	2700	-	Later 'Lucia' RN Depot ship
1909	Asiana	127443	3061	Irvines S/B, W. Hpl	309	T3Cy.	1256	1150	-	
1909	Bendew	127997	3684	Irvines S/B, W. Hpl	312	T3Cy.	1259	1250	-	
1909	Shonga	127994	3044	Irvines S/B, W. Hpl	170	T3Cy.	1260	1550	-	
1909	Winneba	128002	3044	Irvines S/B, W. Hpl	171	T3Cy.	1261	1550	-	
1909	Appenine	127447	3684	Irvines S/B, W. Hpl	311	T3Cy.	1258	1250	-	
1910	Lingfield	129128	4082	Irvines S/B, W. Hpl	493	T3Cy.	1272	1800	-	
1910	American Transport	127467	4763	Irvines S/B, W. Hpl	492	T3Cy.	1271	1700	-	
1910	Glencliffe	124563	3673	Irvines S/B, W. Hpl	486	T3Cy.	1264	1400	-	
1910	Driebergen	Holland	1884	Irvines S/B, W. Hpl	496	T3Cy.	1277	825	-	
1910	Thistletor	123969	4162	Irvines S/B, W. Hpl	495	T3Cy.	1274	1650	-	
1910	Tamele	128032	3924	Irvines S/B, W. Hpl	487	T3Cy.	1265	1700	-	
1910	Indrabarah	131279	7395	Swan, Hunter Nwc	855	T3Cy.	1268	4300	-	Twin screw.
1910	Graanhandel	Holland	1815	Irvines S/B, W. Hpl	490	T3Cy.	1269	825	-	
1910	Berwindmoor	131294	5237	Raylton Dixon, Mbro	553	T3Cy.	1275	2900	-	
1910	Stephen Furness	123969	1710	Irvines S/B, W. Hpl	494	T3Cy.	1273	2650	-	
1910	Akassa	131275	3919	Irvines S/B, W. Hpl	489	T3Cy.	1267	1700	-	
1910	Onitsha	128048	3921	Irvines S/B, W. Hpl	488	T3Cy.	1266	1700	-	
1911	Clan McPhee	129578	5177	Irvines S/B, W. Hpl	499	T3Cy.	1281	3600	-	Sunk 16/8/1940
1911	Zevenbergen	Holland	3003	Irvines S/B, W. Hpl	500	T3Cy.	1282	1200	-	
1911	Nigaristan	128924	4505	Irvines S/B, W. Hpl	505	T3Cy.	1287	2100	-	
1911	Argentine Transport	127465	4763	Irvines S/B, W. Hpl	491	T3Cy.	1270	1700	-	
1911	Manningtry	124297	3869	J.L.Thompson, Sld	477	T3Cy.	1279	1500	-	
1911	Berwindvale	131319	6114	Raylton Dixon, Mbro	554	T3Cy.	1276	2900	-	
1911	Cotovia	132617	4020	Irvines S/B, W. Hpl	506	T3Cy.	1288	1800	-	sunk 22/7/1917
1911	Koophandel	Holland	1736	Irvines S/B, W. Hpl	498	T3Cy.	1280	825	-	
1911	Glenbridge	131837	3845	Irvines S/B, W. Hpl	502	T3Cy.	1284	1400	-	
1911	Brierton	127470	3255	Irvines S/B, W. Hpl	501	T3Cy.	1283	1400	-	sunk 22/11/1916
1911	Glendene	131839	3841	Irvines S/B, W. Hpl	503	T3Cy.	1285	1400	-	
1911	Australian Transport	132812	4773	Irvines S/B, W. Hpl	497	T3Cy.	1278	1700	-	sunk 23/8/1918
1911	Vrijhandel	Holland.	1870	Irvines S/B, W. Hpl	507	T3Cy.	1289	825	-	
1912	La Correntina	131470	8529	Irvines S/B, W. Hpl	516	T3Cy.	1298	5900	-	Twin screw. Sunk 7/10/1914
1912	New Londoner	133504	1374	Irvines S/B, W. Hpl	517	T3Cy.	1299	1850	-	
1912	Black Head	132020	1898	Irvines S/B, W. Hpl	509	T3Cy.	1291	825	-	sunk 1917
1912	El Paraguayo	131434	8508	Irvines S/B, W. Hpl	504	T3Cy.	1286	5900	-	Twin Screw.
1912	Start Point	137512	3840	Irvines S/B, W. Hpl	513	T3Cy.	1295	1800	-	
1912	Cadmus	133003	1879	Irvines S/B, W. Hpl	510	T3Cy.	1292	825	-	
1912	South Point	132814	3837	Irvines S/B, W. Hpl	511	T3Cy.	1293	1800	-	sunk 27/3/1915
1912	Ubbergen	Holland.	1870	Irvines S/B, W. Hpl	508	T3Cy.	1290	825	-	
1912	Saltburn	132813	1768	Raylton Dixon, Mbro	566	T3Cy.	1300	825	-	
1912	West Point	132826	3847	Irvines S/B, W. Hpl	512	T3Cy.	1294	1800	-	sunk 8/10/1916
1913	Orlock Head	132043	1945	Irvines S/B, W.Hpl	535	T3Cy.	2305	850	-	sunk 12/4/1916
1913	Digby	132840	3960	Irvines S/B, W.Hpl	527	T3Cy.	1313	3150	-	12.5 knots on 42 t.p.d.
1913	Garron Head	132037	1933	Irvines S/B, Whpl	532	T3Cy.	2301	875	-	sunk 16/11/1917
1913				Chantiers Penhoet	C3	T3Cy.	1314	-	-	CASTINGS ONLY.
1913	Aeon	132440	3763	Raylton Dixon, Mbro	575	Quad.	1306	2100	-	

EAR SHIP	OFFNO	TONNAGE	BUILDER	YARDNO	TYPE	ENGNO IHP	SHP	REMARKS
13 Westerdijk	Holland	8261	Irvines S/B, W.Hpl	523	Quad.	1308 4250	-	
13 Royal Transport	135895	4652	Irvines S/B, W.Hpl	529	T3Cy.	1318 1650	-	
13			Chantiers Penhoet	D3	T3Cy.	1315 -	-	CASTINGS ONLY.
13 Oldfield Grange	135890	4653	Irvines S/B, W. Hpl	518	T3Cy.	1302 1650	-	sunk 11/2/1917
13 Time	132442	3316	Priestman & Co., Sld	238	Quad.	1301 2500	-	Trials 22.2.1913
13 Clan McBeth	133120	4650	J. Laing. Sld	640	T3Cy.	1312 2000	-	
13 Manchester Civilian	135359	4706	Irvines S/B, W. Hpl	519	T3Cy.	1303 1700	-	
13 Imperial Transport	135892	4648	Irvines S/B, W.Hpl	528	T3Cy.	1317 1650	-	sunk 11/4/1917
13 Ocean Transport	135887	4643	Irvines S/B, W. Hpl	515	T3Cy.	1297 1650	-	
13 Newfield	133516	3847	Irvines S/B, W.Hpl	524	T3Cy.	1309 1400	-	broken up 1966.
13 Troldfos	Norway	1459	Smith's Dock, Mbro	520	T3Cy.	1311 -	-	
13 Elele	135463 ?	4831	Irvines S/B, W. Hpl	521	T3Cy.	1305 2600	-	
13 Tanis /Hambleton Range	135508	4779	Irvines S/B, W.Hpl	525	T3Cy.	1310 1400	-	
13 Oosterdijk	Holland	8251	Irvines S/B, W.Hpl	522	Quad.	1307 4250	-	
13 Eloby	135437	4820	Irvines S/B, W. Hpl	520	T3Cy.	1304 2600	-	
13 Queensland Transport	135881	4669	Irvines S/B, W. Hpl	514	T3Cy.	1296 1650	-	
13 Transmitter	135295	903	Goole S/B & Rep.	-	T3Cy.	2303 750	-	Cable ship:
13 Zeta	Holland	3053	Irvines S/B, W.Hpl	531	T3Cy.	1316 1200	-	
13 Athos	France	12000	Chant. de France	93	T3Cy.	1320 -	-	CASTINGS & FORGINGS ONLY. 2 Sc
14 Cheviot Range	135912	4691	Irvines S/B, W.Hpl	‹543	T3Cy.	2321 1450	-	sunk 21/2/1918
14 Devon	France	9004	At. de France,Dunk'k	98	T3Cy.	2308 5200	-	Twin screw. CASTINGS ONLY.
14 Santeramo	135907	4670	Irvines S/B, W.Hpl	544	T3Cy.	2322 1650	-	
14	France		Chant. de France	100	T3Cy.	2310 5200	-	Twin screw. CASTINGS ONLY.
14 Hambleton Range	135908	4779	Irvines S/B, W.Hpl	542	T3Cy.	2320 1450	-	
14 Panama Transport	135905	4644	Irvines S/B, W.Hpl	539	T3Cy.	2315 1650	-	
14 Orange River	135903	4708	Irvines S/B, W.Hpl	538	T3Cy.	2314 1650	-	
14 Brisbane River	135911	4989	Irvines S/B, W.Hpl	545	T3Cy.	2323 1950	-	sunk 17/4/1917
14 Pengreep	133349	4806	Irvines S/B, W.Hpl	540	T3Cy.	2316 2300	-	
14 Egyptian Transport	135900	4648	Irvines S/B, W.Hpl	530	T3Cy.	1319 1650	-	
14 Delagoa	Denmark	3542	W. Dobson & Co.,	185	T3Cy.	2306 1650	-	
14 Mobile	135902	1905	Irvines S/B, W.Hpl	537	T3Cy.	2313 825	-	sunk 28/4/1915
14 La Perouse	France	9002	At. de France,Dunk'k	99	T3Cy.	2309 5200	-	Twin screw. CASTINGS ONLY.
14 Lowther Castle	135579	4439	Antwerp Eng. Co.	65	T3Cy.	2302 2200	-	
14 Leitrim	139108	9540	Raylton Dixon, Mbro	588	Turb.	2311 -	5400	Twin screw.
14 Castle Eden	135901	1949	Irvines S/B, W.Hpl	536	T3Cy.	2312 825	-	sunk 4/2/1918
14 San Francisco	U.S.A.	5102	N. of Ireland S/B	57	T3Cy.	2304 2700	-	
14 Clutha River	135913	4986	Irvines S/B, W.Hpl	546	T3Cy.	2324 1950	-	
14 Corinthic	136197	4736	Irvines S/B, W.Hpl	541	T3Cy.	2317 1900	-	
14 Magdala	Sweden	3509	N'b'land S/B, Nwc	216	T3Cy.	2307 1650	-	
15 Derwent River	137246	4724	Irvines S/B, W.Hpl	547	T3Cy.	2325 1650	-	
15 Sagama River	137422	4732	Irvines S/B, W.Hpl	550	T3Cy.	2328 1650	-	
15 Swan River	137439	4724	Irvines S/B, W.Hpl	548	T3Cy.	2326 1650	-	sunk 27/9/1917
15 North Western Miller	137431	6504	North'b'ld S/B, Nwc	221	T3Cy.	2318 3000	-	8650 DWT
15 South Western Miller	137462	6514	North'b'ld S/B, Nwc	222	T3Cy.	2319 3000	-	8650 DWT
15 Fraser River	137479	3805	Irvines S/B, W.Hpl	553	T3Cy.	2331 1450	-	
15 Pennar River	137448	3801	Irvines S/B, W.Hpl	552	T3Cy.	2330 1450	-	
15 Gambia River	137470	4729	Irvines S/B, W.Hpl	549	T3Cy.	2327 1650	-	
16 P.32 HMS	Admiralty	613 TD	W. Harkess, Mbro	213	Turb.	2341 -	3500	Twin screw.
16 Aubretia HMS	Admiralty	1320 D	Blyth S/B Co.	193	T4Cy.	2349 2500	-	
16 Mersey River	137511	3806	Irvines S/B, W.Hpl	554	T3Cy.	2332 1450	-	
16 Salvia HMS	Admiralty	1286 D	Irvines S/B, Whpl	577	T4Cy.	2350 2500	-	
16 Wallflower HMS	Admiralty	--	Irvines S/B, W.Hpl	575	T4Cy.	2342 2250	-	
16 Verbena HMS	Admiralty	1250 D	Blyth S/B Co.	192	T4Cy.	2344 2250	-	

MARINE ENGINES BY RICHARDSONS, WESTGARTH (Hartlepool) 1900-1961

YEAR SHIP	OFFNO	TONNAGE	BUILDER	YARDNO	TYPE	ENGNO	IHP	SHP	REMARKS
1916 Boston City	134717	2711	Chas. Hill, Bristol	124	T3Cy.	2346	1500	-	
1916 Start Point	137512	6540	J. Laing, Sld	653	T3Cy.	2336	3500	-	
1916 Batoum				-	T3Cy.	2348	1350	-	re-engining vessel built ..
1916 Westwick	137259	5694	Pickersgill, Sld	192	T3Cy.	2347	2000	-	
1916 Oliphant R.F.A.	139169	4192	Irvines S/B, W.Hpl	557	T3Cy.	2334	2200	-	later 'Palmleaf'. Sunk 2/4/
1916 Valerian HMS	Admiralty	1250 D	Rennoldson, Shields	178	T4Cy.	2345	2250	-	
1916 Wistaria HMS	Admiralty	1250 D	Irvines S/B, W.Hpl	576	T4Cy.	2343	2250	-	
1916 Kepwick Hall	139223	5489	Irvines S/B, W.Hpl	556	T3Cy.	2335	1900	-	
1917 Llanover	140294	4274	Pickersgill, Sld	193	T3Cy.	2359	2150	-	
1917 John Yule	144299	324	Cochrane & Sons,	803	T3Cy.	2378	600	-	'Mersey' Class Trawler (RN)
1917 Lugano	137545	3801	Irvines S/B, W.Hpl	559	T3Cy.	2337	1450	-	
1917 John Quilliam	144374	305	Cochrane & Sons,	801	T3Cy.	2377	600	-	'Mersey' Class Trawler (RN)
1917 Maindy Court	139606	3529	Priestman, Sld	260	T3Cy.	2355	1500	-	
1917 Andrew King	Admiralty	324	Cochrane & Sons,	805	T3Cy.	2379	600	-	'Mersey' Class Trawler (RN)
1917 Anthony Aslett	143820	305	Cochrane & Sons,	689	T3Cy.	2376	600	-	'Mersey' Class Trawler (RN)
1917 William Westenburgh	143929	325	Cochrane & Sons,	687	T3Cy.	2375	600	-	Admiralty Trawler.
1917 Velox HMS	Admiralty	340 D	Wm. Doxford, Sld	516	Turb.	2373	-	-	Twin screw TBD.
1917 Gaillardia HMS	Admiralty	--	Blyth S/B Co.	201	T4Cy	2374	2700	-	
1917 Montbretia HMS	Admiralty	1250 D	Irvines S/B, W.Hpl	588	T4Cy.	2381	2700	-	
1917 PC.66 HMS	Admiralty	694 D	W. Harkess, Mbro	222	Turb.	2382	-	-	
1917 P.46 HMS	Admiralty	613 D	W. Harkess, Mbro	217	Turb.	2351	-	-	
1917 Rapallo	140528	3811	Irvines S/B, W.Hpl	560	T3Cy.	2338	1450	-	
1917 Clan McMaster	140696	6563	Doxford, Sld	481	T3Cy.	2353	2800	-	
1917 Belgol	140377	2648	Irvines S/B, W.Hpl	578	T3Cy.	2358	3375	-	
1917 George Brown	Admiralty	324	Cochrane & Sons,	808	T3Cy.	2380	600	-	'Mersey' Class Trawler (RN)
1918 Roseden	140712	4359	Blyth S/B Co.	194	T3Cy.	2356	1750	-	
1918						2365			CANCELLED.
1918 Wulsty Castle	140576	3566	J.Blumer, Sld	240	Turb.	2359	-	1750	
1918 Clan McMillan	141883	6608	Doxford, Sld	517	T3Cy.	2371	-	-	
1918 Rhododendron HMS	Admiralty	1290 D	Irvines S/B, W.Hpl	591	T4Cy.	2383	2700	-	
1918 Manchester Division	135369	6048	Irvines S/B, W.Hpl	562	T3Cy.	2340	3500	-	
1918 Slavol	142303	2623	Grangemouth S/B Co.	384	T3Cy.	2352	3375	-	
1918						2366			CANCELLED.
1918 New York City	134720	2736	Chas. Hill, Bristol	125	T3Cy.	2357	1650	-	
1918 Grampian Range	140506	4038	Irvines S/B, W.Hpl	551	T3Cy.	2329	1650	-	
1918 Ivy HMS *	Admiralty	1461	Blyth S/B Co.	203	T4Cy.	2384	2700	-	* LR26 Merch. ship 'Ivy'
1918 War Breeze	143110	3095	Irvine's S/B, W.Hpl	599	T3Cy.	2391	2300	-	later 'Withington'
1918						2386			CANCELLED.
1918 Manchester Brigade	135368	6042	Irvines S/B, W.Hpl	561	T3Cy.	2339	3500	-	
1918 War Hamlet	142623	3114	Irvine's S/B, W.Hpl	594	T3Cy.	2389	1750	-	later 'Newcaster'
1918 Bonny	140615	5173	Irvines S/B, W.Hpl	593	T3Cy.	2395	2500	-	ex 'War Stoat'
1918						2364			CANCELLED.
1918 Duquesa	140578	8663	Irvines S/B, W.Hpl	555	T3Cy.	2333	6300	-	Twin screw.
1918 Campfield / Imanol		2847	Furness, Withy, Hpl	213	T3Cy.	2394	800	-	Built 1895(TR): RE-ENGINED *
1918 War Mersey /Clemenceau		2436	H. & C. Grayson	105	T3Cy.	2392	1100	-	
1918						2385			CANCELLED.
1918 War Gurkha	142729	5571	Irvine's S/B, W.Hpl	595	T3Cy.	2388	2700	-	
1918 Persian Prince	140716	5685	Pickersgill, Sld	196	T3Cy.	2370	2750	-	Boilers fitted Sld.
1918 War Brae	142465	3363	Irvine's S/B, W.Hpl	592	T3Cy.	2387	2300	-	later 'Piave' (It.)
1919 Macumba	141935	2526	Chas. Hill, Bristol	134	T3Cy.	2608	1400	-	
1919 Hazelside	142839	3045	Blyth S/B Co.	208	T3Cy.	2601	1550	-	
1919 Portscatho	143497	3071	Irvines S/B, W.Hpl	606	T3Cy.	2609	1550	-	
1919 Trevelyan	142569	5208	Chas. Hill, Bristol	132	T3Cy.	2606	1400	-	

MARINE ENGINES BY RICHARDSONS, WESTGARTH (Hartlepool) 1900-1961

EAR	SHIP	OFFNO	TONNAGE	BUILDER	YARDNO	TYPE	ENGNO	IHP	SHP	REMARKS
919	War Guava	143105	2497	Chas. Hill, Bristol	131	T3Cy.	2605	1400	-	
919	Daybreak	143496	3102	Blyth S/B Co.	210	T3Cy.	2602	1550	-	
919	Badagry	143602	5161	Irvines S/B, W.Hpl	601	T3Cy.	2396	2500	-	ex 'War Crow'
919	Riposto	140660	3044	Irvines S/B, W.Hpl	602	T3Cy.	2398	1550	-	ex 'War Mirage'
919	Bolivian	143618	5116	Irvines S/B, W.Hpl	604	T3Cy.	2399	2500	-	
919	Mackarra	141922	2515	Chas. Hill, Bristol	133	T3Cy.	2607	1400	-	
919	Boutry	143295	5182	Irvine's S/B, W.Hpl	597	T3Cy.	2390	2500	-	ex 'War Gull'
919	Shandon	143369	3069	Irvines S/B, W.Hpl	602	T3Cy.	2397	1550	-	ex 'War Gale'
919	Bristol City	134722	2858	Chas. Hill, Bristol	135	T3Cy.	2612	1650	-	
919	Bereby	143416	5248	Irvines S/B, W.Hpl	600	T3Cy.	2393	2500	-	ex 'War Raven'
920	Notton	144400	3096	Blyth S/B Co.	209	T3Cy.	2603	1550	-	
920	Arlette	France	2701	Chas. Hill, Bristol	138	T3Cy.	2615	1000	-	
920							2401			2401-2600 TO MBRO & SLD WORKS
920	Annik	France	2696	Chas. Hill, Bristol	137	T3Cy.	2614	1000	-	
920	Aviemore	143675	4060	Irvines S/B, W.Hpl	579	T3Cy.	2360	2750	-	
920				Goole S/B., Goole	243		2626			CANCELLED? SHIP NOT BUILT?
920	Boston City	134724	2870	Chas. Hill, Bristol	136	T3Cy.	2613	1650	-	
920	Emlynian	143505	5112	Irvines S/B, W.Hpl	605	T3Cy.	2400	2500	-	ex 'War Unicorn'
920	Evanger	U.S.A.	3869	Irvines S/B., W.Hpl	607	T3Cy.	2627	1950	-	
920	Bygdo	Norway		Chas. Hill, Bristol	139	T3Cy.	2617	950	-	Classed N.V.
920							2625			APPARENTLY CANCELLED
920	Dromore	143691	4096	Irvines S/B, W.Hpl	580	T3Cy.	2361	2750	-	
920	SHIP PROBABLY NOT BLT			Chas. Hill, Bristol	144	T3Cy.	2616	1650	-	144 IN NO YARD LIST.
920	Lorentz W. Hansen	Norway	1918	Chas. Hill, Bristol	140	T3Cy.	2618	950	-	
920	Benares	Sweden	5762	Furness S/B, H.Hill	1	T3Cy.	2619	2750	-	
920	Bachi	Spain	3091	Blyth S/B Co.	211	T3Cy.	2604	1550	-	
920							2611			ENGINE ex Govt. Mach. Store?
920	Incemore	143716	4098	Irvines S/B, W.Hpl	583	T3Cy.	2362	2800	-	
920							2610			ENGINE exGovt. Mach. Store?
920	Peruviana		4099	Irvines S/B, W.Hpl	585	T3Cy.	2363	2800	-	ex 'Jessmore'
921	Abodi Mendi	Spain	5914	Furness S/B, H.Hill	7	T3Cy.	2621	2750	-	ex Sierra Cordoba
921	Westhope	137267	5687	Pickersgill, Sld	195	T3Cy.	2369	2200	-	
921	Vega HMS	Admiralty	340 D	Wm. Doxford, Sld	514	Turb.	2372	-	-	Twin screw TBD
921	Rigi	Norway	5811	Furness S/B, H.Hill	3	T3Cy.	2620	2750	-	
921	Pencarrow	137213	4841	Irvines S/B, W.Hpl	608	T3Cy.	2631	1900	-	
921				North'bld S/B, Nwc	266		2629			CANCELLED - SHIP NOT BUILT.
921				North'bld S/B, Nwc	269		2630			CANCELLED - SHIP NOT BUILT.
921				North'bld S/B, Nwc	262		2628			CANCELLED - SHIP NOT BUILT.
921	London Exchange	145884	6640	Irvines S/B, W.Hpl	586	Turb.	2367	-	3600	ex 'Parisiana'
921	SHIP NOT BUILT.			North'bld S/B,	262	T3Cy.	2628	-	-	YARD LIST STATES CANCELLED.
921	SHIP NOT BUILT.			North'bld S/B,	269	T3Cy.	2630	-	-	YARD LIST STATES CANCELLED.
921	SHIP NOT BUILT.			North'bld S/B,	266	T3Cy.	2629	-	-	YARD LIST STATES CANCELLED.
922	London Corporation	145913	6629	Irvines S/B, W.Hpl	587	T3Cy.	2368	3600	-	ex 'Cynthiana'
922	Bengore Head	145425	2609	Irvines S/B, W.Hpl	610	T3Cy.	2633	1500	-	
922	Baron Vernon	135735	2743	Irvines S/B, W.Hpl	609	T3Cy.	2632	1500	-	ex 'Dunmore Head'
922	Alleghany	145963	3497	Furness S/B, H.Hill	28	T3Cy.	2623	2650	-	
922	Chickahominy	145935	3497	Furness S/B, H.Hill	25	T3Cy.	2622	2650	-	ex 'Persiana'
923	Sycamore	147243	3908	Furness S/B., H.Hill	31	Motor	0			Tosi/Beardmore Diesel
923	Throckley	148045	2866	Furness S/B, H.Hill	49	T3Cy.	2642	1550	-	
923	Kilnsea	147087	5415	Irvines S/B, W.Hpl	611	T3Cy.	2634	1950	-	
923							2638			CANCELLED
923	Kildale	137085	3877	Pickersgill, Sld	206	T3Cy.	2640	1550	-	
923	Artea Mendi	Spain	3554	Chas. Hill, Bristol	143	T3Cy.	2637	1400	-	

MARINE ENGINES BY RICHARDSONS, WESTGARTH (Hartlepool) 1900-1961

YEAR	SHIP	OFFNO	TONNAGE	BUILDER	YARDNO	TYPE	ENGNO	IHP	SHP	REMARKS
1923							2639			CANCELLED
1923	Mountpark / Malm	145583	2699	Chas. Hill, Bristol	141	T3Cy.	2635	1100	-	
1923	Eldon	148044	2867	Furness S/B, H.Hill	48	T3Cy.	2641	1550	-	
1923	Sagaland	Norway	2677	Chas. Hill, Bristol	142	T3Cy.	2636	1100	-	
1923	London Commerce	146693	5650	Furness S/B, H.Hill	34	Turb.	2624	-		5000 Single screw.
1923	SHIP PROBABLY NOT BLT			Goole S/B Co., Goole	243	T3Cy.	2626	-	-	Expected to be classed N.V.
1924	Tramore	147254	3907	Furness S/B., H.Hill	32	Motor	0			Tosi/Beardmore Diesel
1924	Thistleben	146930	4589	Pickersgill, Sld	210	T3Cy.	2643	1727	-	
1924	Corinthic	147155	4823	Irvines S/B, W.Hpl	617	T3Cy.	2644	2100	-	
1924	Kamloops	147682	2402	Furness S/B, H.Hill	68	T3Cy.	2645	850	-	
1924	Lethbridge	147702	2407	Furness S/B, H.Hill	69	T3Cy.	2646	850	-	
1925	Manchester Citizen	147409	5328	Furness S/B, H.Hill	80	T3Cy.	2649	3800	-	
1925	City of Toronto	152838	1688	Davie S/B,Lauzon PQ	490	T3Cy.	2652	850	-	
1925	Manchester Commerce	147408	5328	Furness S/B, H.Hill	79	T3Cy.	2648	3800	-	
1925		France		Chant. Gironde, Bdx	-	T3Cy.	2653	-	-	CASTINGS ONLY: SEE No.2650
1925	City of Kingston	152837	1690	Davie S/B,Lauzon PQ	489	T3Cy.	2651	850	-	
1925	Winnipeg	152854	2383	Davie S/B,Lauzon PQ	493	T3Cy.	2654	850	-	
1925	Ashleigh	148560	4853	Furness S/B, H.Hill	77	T3Cy.	2647	2700	-	
1925	Aramis / Chenonceaux	France	14825	Chant. Gironde, Bdx	178	T3Cy.	2650	-	-	Twin S.CASTINGS & DRAW'GS ONLY
1926	Selkirk	152859	2384	Davie S/B,Lauzon PQ	494	T3Cy.	2655	850	-	
1926	Talang Akar	Holland	2041	Furness S/B, H.Hill	107	T3Cy.	2658	-	-	
1927	Gypsum King	147786	3915	Furness S/B, H.Hill	108	T3Cy.	2656	1800	-	
1927	Gypsum Prince	147789	3915	Furness S/B, H.Hill	112	T3Cy.	2660	1800	-	
1927	Gypsum Queen	147787	3915	Furness S/B, H.Hill	109	T3Cy.	2657	1800	-	
1927	St. Lawrence	153438	6328	Davie S/B,Lauzon PQ	495	T4Cy.	2661	2900	-	Twin Screw.
1928	City of Montreal	153442	1665	Midland S/B, Ontario	19	T3Cy.	2663	850	-	
1928	Quebec	153450	7016	Davie S/B,Lauzon PQ	497	T4Cy.	2669	5000	-	
1928	Saskatoon	153436	2412	Midland S/B, Ontario	20	T3Cy.	2664	850	-	
1928	City of Hamilton	153423	1665	Midland S/B, Ontario	18	T3Cy.	2662	850	-	
1928	British Justice	160548	6982	Palmers S/B, Jarrow	977	Motor	2667	-		2500 Tanker
1928	Weyburn	153437	2408	Midland S/B, Ontario	21	T3Cy.	2665	850	-	
1928	PROTOTYPE ENGINE		-----	-----------------	----	Motor	3000			
1928	British Renown	160397	6998	J. Laing, Sld	700	Motor	2659	-		2500 continued in service 30yrs+
1928	British Freedom	160493	6985	Palmers S/B, Jarrow	968	Motor	2666	-		2500 Tanker.
1928	Tadoussac	153447	7013	Davie S/B,Lauzon PQ	497	T4Cy.	2668	5000	-	
1929	Cingalese Prince	161263	6625	Blythswood S/B. Gsw	23	Motor	2671	-		6000 Twin screw.
1929	Hadiotis	Greece	4386	Northbld S/B, Nwc	404	T3Cy.	2670	2150	-	
1929	City of Windsor	154463	1905	Davie S/B,Lauzon PQ	501	T3Cy.	2673	850	-	
1929	Irania		2186	Blythswood, Ggw		Motor	3001	1250		Tanker. 1st 'Burn' Engine.
1929	Silverpalm	161341	6373	J.L.Thompson, Sld	566	Motor	2674	-		5750 Twin screw.
1929	Siamese Prince	161297	6607	Blythswood S/B. Gsw	24	Motor	2672	-		6000 Twin screw.
1930	Silverwillow	161424	6373	J.L.Thompson, Sld	568	Motor	2675	-		5750 Twin screw.
1931	Vestfold	Panama	14547	Furness S/B, H.Hill	189	Quad.	2677	6000	-	
1931	British Strength	162575	7139	Palmers S/B, Jarrow	1005	Motor	2676	-		2850 Tanker
1931	Svend Foyn	162742	14596	Furness S/B, H.Hill	190	Quad.	2678	6000	-	
1933	St. Germain ex Epoca	135618	1044	Karlshamn Verks,1924	1036	Motor	3002	1000		Blt '24:NE'33:later re-eng.
1934	Silverpine	147671	5066	Swan Hunter,Nwc 1924	1231	Motor	3003	4000		Ship built 1924, NE 1934
1934	Silverlarch	147710	5064	Swan Hunter,Nwc 1924	1233	Motor	3005	4000		Ship built 1924, NE 1934
1936	Starcross	162115	4662	J.L.Thompson, Sld	576	T3Cy.	2681	1250	-	
1936	Syrian Prince	165353	1990	Furness S/B, H.Hill	262	T3Cy.	2679	1700	-	
1937	Seagull HMS	Admiralty	835 D	Devonport Dockyard	-	Turb.	2684	-	1750	
1937	Northleigh	165573	5450	Pickersgill, Sld	237	T3Cy.	2686	2000	-	
1937	Leda HMS	Admiralty	835 D	Devonport Dockyard	-	Turb.	2683	-	1750	Twin screw.

YEAR	SHIP	OFFNO	TONNAGE	BUILDER	YARDNO	TYPE	ENGNO	IHP	SHP	REMARKS
1937	Cyprian Prince	165374	1988	Furness S/B, H.Hill	263	T3Cy.	2680	1700	-	
1937	Haughton Hall	164335	5103	J. Laing, Sld	714	T3Cy.	2682	1950	-	
1938	Starstone	166528	5702	Doxford, Sld	645	T3Cy.	2691	2150	-	
1938	Ellin	Greece	4917	Bartram, Sld	278	T3Cy.	2688	1800	-	
1938	Goodleigh	166586	5468	Pickersgill, Sld	240	T3Cy.	2693	2000	-	
1938	Rebeca	Holland	3170	Furness S/B, H.Hill	277	T3Cy.	2689	2300	-	Twin screw tanker.
1938	Rosalia	Holland	3177	Furness S/B, H.Hill	278	T3Cy.	2690	2300	-	Twin screw tanker.
1938	Chulmleigh	166440	5445	Pickersgill, Sld	238	T3Cy.	2687	2000	-	
1938	Themoni	Greece	5719	Doxford, Sld	646	T3Cy.	2692	2150	-	
1938	Port St. John	166332	5668	J.L.Thompson, Sld	579	Motor	2685	-	4250	
1940	Charlton Hall	166303	5200	J. Laing, Sld	731	T3Cy.	2696	1800	-	
1940	Daydawn	167798	4768	Pickersgill, Sld	241	T3Cy.	2697	1450	-	
1940	Winkleigh	167425	5468	Pickersgill, Sld	242	T3Cy.	2694	1900	-	
1941	Empire Mica	164846	8032	Furness S/B, H.Hill	328	T3Cy.	2702	3650	-	Tanker
1941	St. Essylt	162150	5634	J.L.Thompson, Sld	600	Motor	2695	-	3200	
1941	Empire Oil	164845	8029	Furness S/B, H.Hill	327	T3Cy.	2701	3650	-	Tanker
1941							2707			NOT USED.
1941	Erne HMS	Admiralty	1250 D	Furness S/B, H.Hill	317	Turb.	2698	-	4300	Ref. T.314
1941	Empire Emerald	164849	8032	Furness S/B, H.Hill	334	T3Cy.	2705	3650	-	
1941							2706			NOT USED.
1941	Empire Amethyst	164848	8032	Furness S/B, H.Hill	330	T3Cy.	2704	3650	-	
1941							2709			NOT USED.
1941	Empire Celt	164851	8032	Furness S/B, H.Hill	335	T3Cy.	2710	3650	-	
1941							2708			NOT USED.
1941	Empire Sapphire	164847	8031	Furness S/B, H.Hill	329	T3Cy.	2703	3650	-	Tanker
1941	Ibis HMS	Admiralty	1250 D	Furness S/B, H.Hill	318	Turb.	2699	-	4300	Ref. T.315
1941	Empire Gold	164843	8028	Furness S/B, H.Hill	325	T3Cy.	2700	3650	-	sunk 18/4/45
1942				Furness S/B., H.Hill			2718			TRANSFERRED TO N.E.M.
1942	Empire Grenadier	164859	9811	Furness S/B, H.Hill	344	T3Cy.	2717	3650	-	Tanker
1942	British Nugget	164860	9807	Furness S/B, H.Hill	349	T3Cy.	2729	3600	-	
1942							2721			TRANSFERRED TO N.E.M.
1942							2724			TRANSFERRED TO N.E.M.
1942	Eaglesdale	168248	8032	Furness S/B, H.Hill	339	T3Cy.	2711	3650	-	ex 'Empire Metal'
1942							2725			TRANSFERRED TO N.E.M.
1942	Empire Beaumont	164854	7044	Furness S/B, H.Hill	345	T3Cy.	2719	2500	-	
1942	Empire Lytton	164858	9807	Furness S/B, H.Hill	343	T3Cy.	2716	3650	-	
1942	Empire Norseman	164855	9811	Furness S/B, H.Hill	342	T3Cy.	2715	3650	-	Tanker
1942							2723			TRANSFERRED TO N.E.M.
1942	Empire Cobbett	164861	9811	Furness S/B, H.Hill	350	T3Cy.	2730	3600	-	
1942	Empire Dickens	164853	9819	Furness S/B, H.Hill	341	T3Cy.	2713	3650	-	Tanker
1942							2722			TRANSFERRED TO N.E.M.
1942	Empire Granite	164844	8028	Furness S/B, H.Hill	326	T3Cy.	2714	2800	-	Poss. re-build of 1926 eng.?
1942	Easedale	168256	8032	Furness S/B, H.Hill	340	T3Cy.	2712	3650	-	
1942	Empire Guidon	164857	7041	Furness S/B, H.Hill	346	T3Cy.	2720	2500	-	
1943	Empire Bounty	169126	8128	Furness S/B, H.Hill	356	Turb.	2740	-	6800	
1943	British Vigour	168398	5844	Furness S/B, H.Hill	347	Motor	2727	-	2500	Tanker
1943	Lafian	168857	7221	Furness S/B, H.Hill	352	T3Cy.	2732	2200	-	
1943	British Purpose	168424	5852	Furness S/B, H.Hill	348	Motor	2728	-	2500	Tanker
1943					-	T3Cy.	2733	2200	-	ENGINES ONLY SUPPLIED.
1943	Empire Regent	164865	9904	Furness S/B, H.Hill	355	Turb.	2739	-	6800	
1943	Kumasian	168351	7221	Furness S/B, H.Hill	351	T3Cy.	2731	2200	-	
1943	Empire Viceroy	169036	7803	Vickers, Barrow	858	Turb.	2734	-		8000 HP, IP & LP TURBINES.
1943	Empire Chieftain	164863	9904	Furness S/B, H.Hill	354	Turb.	2738	-	6800	

MARINE ENGINES BY RICHARDSONS, WESTGARTH (Hartlepool) 1900-1961

YEAR SHIP	OFFNO	TONNAGE	BUILDER	YARDNO	TYPE\ENGNO	IHP	SHP	REMARKS
1943 Empire Law	169132	8127	Furness S/B, H.Hill	357	Turb. 2741	-	6800	Tanker
1944 Empire Protector	169147	8157	Furness S/B, H.Hill	360	Turb. 2746	-	6800	Tanker
1944 Empire Paladin	169146	8141	Furness S/B, H.Hill	359	Turb. 2745	-	6800	Tanker
1944 Empire Paragon	180138	9888	J. Laing, Sld	751	Turb. 2735	-		8000 HP, IP & LP TURBINES.
1944 Wave Emperor	180034	8196	Furness S/B, H.Hill	361	Turb. 2748	-	6800	
1944 Terborch	Holland	9894	Caledon S/B, Dundee	405	Turb. 2737	-	6800	later 'Eemdijk'
1944 Empire Dynasty	169038	9896	J.L.Thompson, Sld	631	Turb. 2744	-	6800	
1944 Empire Kitchener	166218	9881	Caledon S/B, Dundee	406	Turb. 2747	-	6800	
1944 Empire Milner	169143	8135	Furness S/B, H.Hill	358	Turb. 2742	-	6800	Tanker
1944 Empire Captain	166217	9875	Caledon S/B, Dundee	404	Turb. 2736	-	6800	
1944 Wave Governor	180489	8190	Furness S/B, H.Hill	362	Turb. 2751	-	6800	
1945 Empire Life	166220	9381	Caledon S/B, Dundee	407	Turb. 2750	-	6800	
1945 Bencruachan	181174	8047	J.L.Thompson, Sld	644	Turb. 2762	-	6800	
1945 Wave Regent	180564	8184	Furness S/B, H.Hill	363	Turb. 2752	-	6800	
1945 Wave Ruler	180849	8138	Furness S/B, H.Hill	373	Turb. 2755	-	6800	ex 'Empire Evesham'
1945				-	Turb. 2758	-	6800	TURBINES & GEARING TO HOLLAND.
1945 Wave Sovereign	180813	8182	Furness S/B, H.Hill	364	Turb. 2754	-	6800	
1945 Empire Athelstan	169213	7795	Vickers, Walker	94	Turb. 2759	-	6800	Turbines ex Metro-Vickers.
1945 City of Durham	169434	10024	Cammell Laird, B'hd	1133	Turb. 2749	-	6800	
1945				-	Turb. 2757	-	6800	TURBINES & GEARING TO HOLLAND.
1945 Empire Admiral	180145	7884	Vickers, Barrow	859	Turb. 2743	-	6800	
1946 Wave Baron	180885	8174	Furness S/B, H.Hill	378	Turb. 2756	-	6800	Turb. by Metro-Vickers.
1946 British Ensign	181615	8738	Furness S/B, H.Hill	393	Motor 2768	-	3100	Eng. by Doxfords (258).Tanker.
1946 British Admiral	181504	8738	Furness S/B, H.Hill	390	Motor 2764	-	3100	Eng. by Doxfords(253).Tanker.
1946 British Empress	181583	8745	Furness S/B, H.Hill	391	Motor 2765	-	3100	Eng. by Doxfords(253).Tanker.
1946 Empire Bounty(Eng2740)		8128	Furness S/B, H.Hill	356	2761	-	-	1 SET GEARING & CASE re 2740
1946 Empire Ethelbert	Norway *	7843	Vickers, Walker	95	Turb. 2760	-	6800	*'Beljeanne'. Turb.Metro-Vick.
1946 Wave Premier	181515	8175	Furness S/B, H.Hill	389	Turb. 2753	-	6800	
1946 Asia	181080	8723	J. Laing, Sld	769	Turb. 2763	-	7250	
1947 Sherbro	181103	4811	Furness S/B, H.Hill	405	Motor 2772	-	3100	
1947 Arabia	182394	8720	J. Laing, Sld	774	Turb. 2767	-	7250	
1947 British Isles	181703	8738	Furness S/B, H.Hill	394	Motor 2769	-	3100	Eng. by Doxfords (258).Tanker.
1947 Sekondi	182402	4811	Furness S/B, H.Hill	406	Motor 2773	-	3100	Eng. Type 56LB4
1947 sent to Holland.				-	Turb. 2766	-	6800	TURB., GEAR'G & B'LERS SENT.
1947 Standard Gearing etc				-	2770	-	-	AS FOR CARGO LINER/TANKER
1947 Empire Bounty see 2740		8128	Furness S/B, H.Hill	356	Turb. 2771	-	-	c/w Pipework.
1948 Bogesund	Sweden	1351	Furness S/B, H.Hill	418	Motor 2777	-	1350	INSTALL ONLY.
1948 Bergsund	Sweden	1352	Furness S/B, H.Hill	417	Motor 2776	-	1350	INSTALL ONLY.
1948 British Venture	182921	6119	J.L.Thompson, Sld	656	Motor 2775	-	2500	Tanker. Eng.Type 60LB4
1948 Svanesund	Sweden	1352	Furness S/B, H.Hill	420	Motor 2779	-	1350	INSTALL ONLY.
1948 Svensksund	Sweden	1352	Furness S/B, H.Hill	419	Motor 2778	-	1350	INSTALL ONLY.
1948 Vikdal	Norway	4779	Hall, Russell, Abdn	806	Motor 2774	-	3250	ENGINE ON BEDPLATE ONLY.
1949 Flamingo	Sweden	1351	Furness S/B, H.Hill	422	Motor 2781	-	1350	INSTALL ONLY.
1949 Folias	Sweden	1351	Furness S/B, H.Hill	421	Motor 2780	-	1350	INSTALL ONLY.
1950 Assyria	183787	8683	Swan Hunter, Nwc	1801	Turb. 2782	-	7250	
1952 Carl Schmedenham	Panama	9918	Vickers, Barrow	1008	Turb. 2784	-	6600	TURB. & GEARING SENT BARROW.
1952					2785			NOT USED.
1953 Caltex Perth	185987	11746	Furness S/B, H.Hill	458	Turb. 2786	7300	-	*45,000 lbs/hr.Tanker. V. Prop
1953 Caltex Canberra	185871	11746	Furness S/B, H.Hill	442	Turb. 2783	-	7300	*45,000 lbs/hr.Tanker. V.Prop.
1954 Melika	Liberia	20551	Furness S/B, H.Hill	462	Turb. 2787	-	12500	* 55,000 lbs/hr.
1955 Samuel Ugelstad	Norway	21178	Furness S/B, H.Hill	472	Turb. 2792	-	12500	* 55,000 lbs/hr.
1955 Sirius	Sweden	16056	Furness S/B, H.Hill	467	Turb. 2788	-	7300	* 45,000 lbs/hr.
1955 Sept Iles	188191	21053	Furness S/B, H.Hill	471	Turb. 2791	-	12500	* 55,000 lbs/hr.

MARINE ENGINES BY RICHARDSONS, WESTGARTH (Hartlepool) 1900-1961

AR SHIP	OFFNO	TONNAGE	BUILDER	YARDNO	TYPE	ENGNO	IHP	SHP	REMARKS
56 London Valour	187505	16268	Furness S/B, H.Hill	475	Turb.	2790	-	7300	* 45,000 lbs/hr. Var. Prop.
56 Panaghia	Liberia	16009	Furness S/B, H.Hill	469	Turb.	2789	-	7300	* 45,000 lbs/hr. Var. Prop.
56 Virginia	Liberia	11623	Furness S/B, H.Hill	483	Turb.	2798	-	7300	* 45,000 lbs/hr.
57 Overseas Pioneer	300801	167267	Furness S/B, H.Hill	477	Turb.	2795	-	7300	* 45,000 lbs/hr. Var.Prop.
57 Arabian Gulf	Liberia	20504	Furness S/B, H.Hill	473	Turb.	2793	-	12500	* 55,000 lbs/hr.
57						2801			NOT USED.
57 London Resolution	187689	16269	Furness S/B, H.Hill	479	Turb.	2796	-	7300	* 45,000 lbs/hr. Var. Prop.
57						2799			NOT USED.
57						2800			NOT USED.
57 Violetta	Liberia	11624	Furness S/B, H.Hill	481	Turb.	2797	-	7300	* 45,000 lbs/hr.
57 San Edmondo	187630	11486	Furness S/B, H.Hill	496	Turb.	2803		7500	* 45,000 lbs/hr. Tanker.
57 London Tradition	187664	16275	Furness S/B, H.Hill	476	Turb.	2794	-	7300	* 45,000 lbs/hr. Var.Prop.
58 Overseas Explorer	300836	16267	Furness S/B, H.Hill	461	Turb.	2802	-	7300	* 45,000 lbs/hr. Var. Prop.
58 Belgulf Glory	Belgium	12018	Furness S/B, H.Hill	497	Turb.	2804	-	7300	* 45,000 lbs/hr.Tanker. V.Prop
59 Belgulf Progress	Belgium	12018	Furness S/B, H.Hill	498	Turb.	2805	-	7300	* 45,000 lbs/hr. Tanker.
59 Gulf Briton	302593	26298	Furness S/B, H.Hill	506	Turb.	2807	-	17500	*72,500 lbs/hr. Tanker.
59			Furness S/B., H.Hill	503		2806			CANCELLED.
60 Gulf Dane	302859	26652	Furness S/B, H.Hill	508	Turb.	2809	-	17500	*72,500 lbs/hr. Tanker.
60 Gulf Scot	302745	26652	Furness S/B, H.Hill	507	Turb.	2808	-	17500	*72,500 lbs/hr. Tanker.
61			Furness S/B., H.Hill	510		2811			CANCELLED.
61 Gulf Finn	304438	25299	Furness S/B, H.Hill	509	Turb.	2810	-	17500	*72,500 lbs/hr. Tanker.

APPENDIX IV

RICHARDSON & WESTGARTH ITEMS IN THE COLLECTIONS OF THE HARTLEPOOL MUSEUM SERVICE

Printed Ephemera

1)	— 63'77 Boxes 16-21	Robert Wood Collection Including materials relevant to the firm's early days and immediate precursors (viz. Richardson Duck & Co.)
2)	— Box E2	Includes Richardsons, Westgarth promotional material from 1960's.
3)	— Box 39 60'93'1	Consists of Brochures and Specifications.

Photographic Items

4)	— 9 Albums 1'82	Includes photographs numbers 754-1424 giving detailed views of the factory from the 1940's to the 1950's.
5)	— Box 25	Includes the Richardsons, Westgarth material, e.g. shots of Boilers and the Boiler Shop, social gatherings, etc.
6)	— 60'93'2 :	a) and b) deal with the equipping of the Trawsfynnydd Nuclear Power Station and c) shows various jobs in progress.
7)	— T1903-17	Photographs of the dismantling of the Electricity Sub-Station.

Scale Models

8)	— T1709	Turbine Engine Model 75005 HP, 1946.
9)	— T2017	Model of a Turbo-Alternator, 117 megawatts.
10)	— T1967	Foster-Wheeler Boiler manufactured at Hartlepool.
11)	— T1968	A Triple Expansion Engine 1927, probably Richardsons, Westgarth.

Richardson & Westgarth Equipment

12)	— T1969	Electricity Sub-Station, Richardson & Westgarth, Middleton: facia and dials, etc.